BIG

BULKBUILDING INSTRUCTIONAL GUIDE

by Ellington Darden, Ph.D.
Photography by Chris Lund

A Perigee Book

Perigee Books
are published by
The Putnam Publishing Group
200 Madison Avenue
New York, NY 10016

Library of Congress
Cataloging-in-Publication Data

Darden, Ellington, 1943- .
   Big : bulkbuilding instructional guide /
by Ellington Darden.
      p.   cm.
   1. Bodybuilding   I. Title
GV546.5.D353   1990   90-35321   CIP
646.7′5—dc20
ISBN 0-399-51630-1

Printed in the United States of America

   3   4   5   6   7   8   9   10

This book is printed on acid-free paper.
∞

Other Books of Interest
by ELLINGTON DARDEN, Ph.D.

Massive Muscles in 10 Weeks
Super High-Intensity Bodybuilding
The Nautilus Diet
How to Lose Body Fat
Conditioning for Football
The Athlete's Guide to Sports Medicine
The Nautilus Book
The Nautilus Nutrition Book
The Nautilus Woman
The Nautilus Bodybuilding Book
The Nautilus Advanced Bodybuilding Book
The Six-Week Fat-to-Muscle Makeover
Big Arms in Six Weeks
100 High-Intensity Ways to Improve Your
   Bodybuilding
32 Days to a 32-Inch Waist
New High-Intensity Bodybuilding

WARNING!
The high-intensity routines in this book are
intended only for healthy men and women.
People with health problems should not
follow these routines without a physician's
approval. Before beginning any exercise or
dietary program, always consult with your
doctor.

For a free catalog of Dr. Darden's books,
please send a self-addressed, stamped
envelope to Nautilus Sports/Medical
Industries, P.O. Box 160, Independence, VA
24348.

CONTENTS

GET BIG!

QUESTION: In the last ten years, what's the most significant muscle-building discovery?

ANSWER: Super-slow training, whereby you perform each repetition in a slow, deliberate style. You lift the weight in approximately 10 seconds, and lower it in five seconds.

If you've never trained using the super-slow style, and few bodybuilders have, then you're in for a surprise. Properly performed, super-slow repetitions will stimulate the maximum amount of muscle growth in the shortest possible time. It's an almost unbelievable way to pack on pounds of solid muscle.

When super slow is combined with the correct nutritional plan, it provides the very best mode of bulking your arms, shoulders, chest, back, thighs, and calves—quickly!

Witness the effect that super-slow training had on Eddie Mueller's physique. Some of you may remember Eddie from one of my previous books: *Massive Muscles in 10 Weeks.* In 1986 Eddie went through a ten-week program and increased his body weight from 160 to 176 pounds. None of his training was performed in the super-slow style.

Vince Taylor is huge—HUGE BY CHOICE
because he understands and applies proper
diet and proper exercise.

Gary Strydom is well known for his massive shoulder development. Jim Quinn is in the background.

8

Eddie Mueller as he looked before and after the Six-Week Bulkbuilding program featured in this book. Eddie gained 19½ pounds of body weight and added 1½ inches to his upper arms, 5 inches to his chest, and 4⅞ inches to his thighs.

Ray Mentzer is impressed by the biceps of Bertil Fox.

He put on 16 pounds in ten weeks. But that was three years ago. Could super slow produce similar, or better, growth in Eddie's physique?

Eddie arrived in Dallas weighing 172.5 pounds at a height of 5 feet 8¼ inches. Mostly training on his own since we completed the 1986 study, Eddie had not been able to keep his previous weight of 176 pounds.

"I just can't train myself and get much out of it," Eddie commented. "And I have to be really pushed to eat enough calories to keep my weight up. That's why I'm in Dallas. I know you can motivate me in both areas."

Eddie's exact workouts and eating plans are listed in Part II, but here's a preview of what he accomplished.

In six weeks Eddie's body weight went from 172.5 to 192, a gain of 19.5 pounds. He added 1½ inches to his upper arms, 5 inches to his chest, and 4⅞ inches to his thighs.

The remarkable thing is that Eddie achieved better results from six weeks of super-slow training than he did from ten weeks of conventional high-intensity exercise. The super-slow results are even more significant when you consider that the last 16 pounds took Eddie's muscle mass to levels previously not reached, or closer to his genetic potential. Rate of growth slows as it nears the maximum.

From the before-and-after photographs, you can see that Eddie cer-

Nimrod King displays the ultimate in BIG arms.

tainly put on the mass. "All my life I've wanted to be BIG," smiled Eddie. "Super slow helped me reach my goal."

If getting BIG is your goal, then this course is perfect for you.

Part I brings back the concept of bulking up. The idea is that being massively big is healthier, and more fun, than the current vogue of being ripped to shreds.

Part II describes the super-slow techniques and routines, as well as eating plans, that Eddie Mueller applied for his phenomenal gains.

IT'S TIME FOR YOU TO:
GET INSPIRED,
GET MOTIVATED,
AND
GET BIG!

Mike Christian has come as close as any professional bodybuilder to reaching his genetic potential.

BIG!
PART I
THE WHY

Brian Buchanan assists Mike Christian in doing a few more repetitions for his awesome arms and shoulders.

BIG.

CHAPTER 1
WHY BULKBUILDING?

Bulkbuilding is serious business for Mike Christian.

The impressive right arm of Franco Santoriello.

BIG

You want to get BIG, and I don't blame you.

When I started weight training in the summer of 1959, my skinny body (all 130 pounds of me) desperately wanted to be big. I was entering the ninth grade and football season was only a few months away. Bigger, stronger muscles would definitely be an asset on the football field, not to mention on the beach, or in the neighborhood.

The first muscle magazines that I looked through contained pictures of men who were big beyond belief: men such as Clancy Ross, Bill Pearl, Leroy Colbert, George Effierman, and Marvin Eder. These men were

Pulley rows work many small muscles of the upper back.

not concerned about being ripped. In fact, I don't believe the word was even applied to bodybuilding in the fifties and sixties. What interested trainees wanted then was bulk, size, and mass.

In simple terms, we wanted to get BIG, really BIG!

"I've always admired that big, bulky look," Chris Lund said to me recently as we discussed the concept of this book. Chris has photographed all the major bodybuilding contests and has contributed to many of my books. "That look got me into bodybuilding over twenty years ago. In those days you could train with high intensity and eat with even higher intensity. You know, a few pints of beer, lots of milk, potatoes, and gravy, and thick steaks. You felt as big and powerful as you looked, because you were. Those were the days!"

Chris is right. There's something about being big and strong and bulky that's hard to explain unless you've experienced it. It's a state that's unmatched by other things. It's a great feeling of well-being and superiority.

Chris Lund and I are annoyed and sick of the super-ripped look. Yes, you need definition and muscularity. But carried to extremes, which is what most champions do, the look—and diet and chemicals re-

The massive physique of Lee Haney offers an interesting comparison to the symmetrical body of Lee Labrada.

quired to get it—is *unnatural* and *unhealthy*.

Even under the best conditions, most trainees simply do *not* have the genetic capabilities of getting extremely ripped. They would be much better off training for size, combined with a reasonable amount of definition.

Big, massive muscles—bulk-building.

That's what this book is about.

Sandy Riddell works her triceps.

Keep your elbows wide when doing the dumbbell bench press.

BIG!

CHAPTER 2
BIGGER IS BETTER

Mike Quinn will testify to the fact that *Bigger Is Better.*

One of the primary goals of body-building is to take your muscles to a level of physical development that transcends the norm. If you fail in this mission, then you will not be a successful bodybuilder.

The benefits of getting a bigger, stronger body are many.

HERCULES, THE ULTIMATE BODYBUILDER

The famous Greek statue of Hercules represents the ultimate in bodybuilding. Even today's great champions look in awe at this Olympian god, carrying their admiration for his massive musculature into the training gyms and attempting to emulate his appearance.

Examine the massive deltoids of Hercules, his incredibly thick forearms and quadriceps. This was a bodybuilder's bodybuilder.

The herculean physique of Daryl Stafford.

Henderson Thorne has a unique blend of mass and power.

Mr. Olympia winner Lee Haney is one of the largest men in professional bodybuilding.

34

As Arthur Jones, the inventor of Nautilus equipment, once said: "For an ancient sculptor to create this body of Hercules out of stone meant that there actually existed a man of his proportions, because no anatomy books or charts existed during those times."

To achieve the massiveness of Hercules is an unrealistic goal for most people. Most people interested in bodybuilding can get big, much bigger than they realize, but mass of herculean proportions is only obtainable by a few. If you have the genetic potential to look like Hercules, then this book will help you reach your goal in the most efficient and effective manner. Even if you don't have excessive size in your family tree, you can still get bigger faster with this program than with others.

INTENSITY POWER

Intensity is a state of mind, a level of mental power that enables you to work through the pain barrier. The power of intensity is what makes it possible for you to achieve growth stimulation, and ultimately the size you want. To become big you must constantly overload your muscles, you must use progressively heavier and heavier weights. Once a heavy weight has been conquered—and it *must* be conquered—ascend to the next level of intensity with still heavier weights.

Fighting, clawing, brushing aside the pain of lactic acid buildup, ever striving for that last repetition, literally forcing movement into unyielding iron—that's what intensity is, and that's what it takes to achieve massive muscles.

With continued training and this kind of intense determination, don't you think that there's carryover into other areas of your life? Don't you believe your approach to difficult tasks is less fraught with worry, doubt, and lack of self-confidence?

Yes. Intense determination is a major factor in becoming successful in bodybuilding and in life.

CONNECTIVE TISSUE STRENGTH

Overload is the common denominator in all forms of productive exercise. Without overload, your muscles cannot grow, your ligaments and tendons cannot get thicker and stronger, and your bones cannot become denser and capable of withstanding greater force.

What type of exercise delivers the greatest positive overload, the kind that forces the greatest level of adaptive growth? Of course, it's weight training. And what type of weight training delivers maximum

Front raises are a great exercise for the deltoids.

36

Ian Harrison of England
has a massive physique.

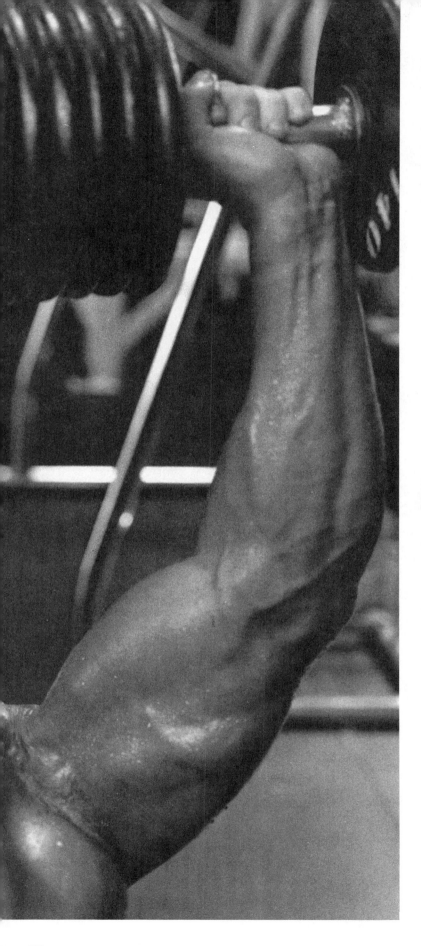

overload? High-intensity weight training.

Doesn't it logically follow that training for size will give your tendons, ligaments, connective tissues, and muscles the most strength? And won't the increased thickness and tensile strength result in fewer injuries, less chance of sprains, strains, and outright tears?

The answer is yes. Bigger, stronger muscles are the single most effective deterrent to injury for athletes of all sports. Injury-free bodybuilding also relates to unimpeded training for greater gains.

NEUROMUSCULAR EFFICIENCY

Muscles contract as a result of electrochemical discharge in their cells. The nerves transport this charge to the muscles, and their efficiency in carrying it can be greatly enhanced through training.

Remember when you did a bench press for the first time? It was difficult to coordinate the movement without bobbing and weaving, wasn't it? Such lack of coordination occurred because your neuromuscular pathways, which control your movements, had not yet become fine-tuned. Soon, however, with practice, you were able to bench press much more weight than you began with. Yes, you probably had developed more muscle, but some of your strength improvement was related to your neuromuscular pathways becoming more efficient. You had become more skillful at the bench press.

This motor skill development continues throughout your body-building life. As you get stronger, you handle more weight, which in turn facilitates nervous input. With proper progression, this spiral continues upward until you can handle some really massive weights.

PSYCHOLOGICAL EFFECTS

There is a definite psychological accomplishment that you get from lifting a heavy weight, especially one that you've not succeeded at lifting previously. Maybe it's a personal record in the bench press, squat, or curl. Or maybe you just did more chin-ups than ever before. Whether it's weight, repetitions, or a combination of both, most body-builders get a long-lasting high from breaking records.

The feeling of conquest after bettering a training record may be similar to what any great artist must feel after creating a masterpiece. The beauty of this feeling is that it never goes away. Once you've done it, it energizes you for the rest of your days. It spurs you on to even greater

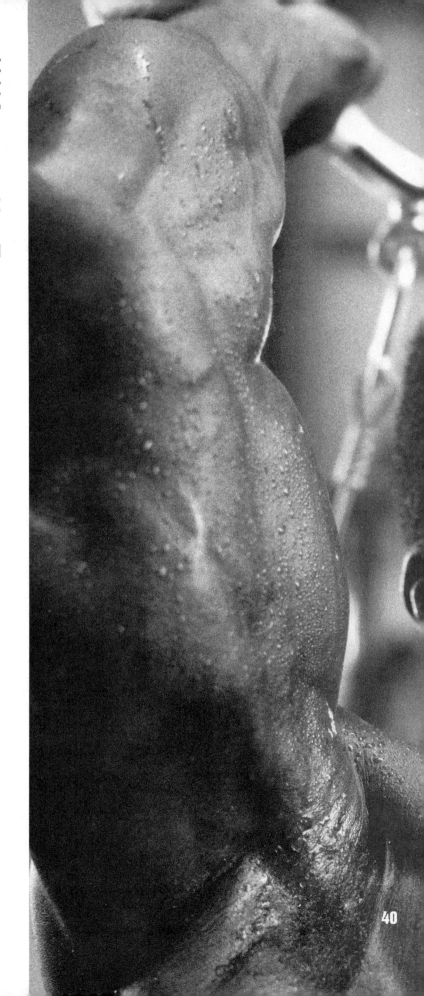

Robby Robinson trains triceps.

Strive to be progressive in all your exercise.

42

43

Adhere to strict form on each repetition.

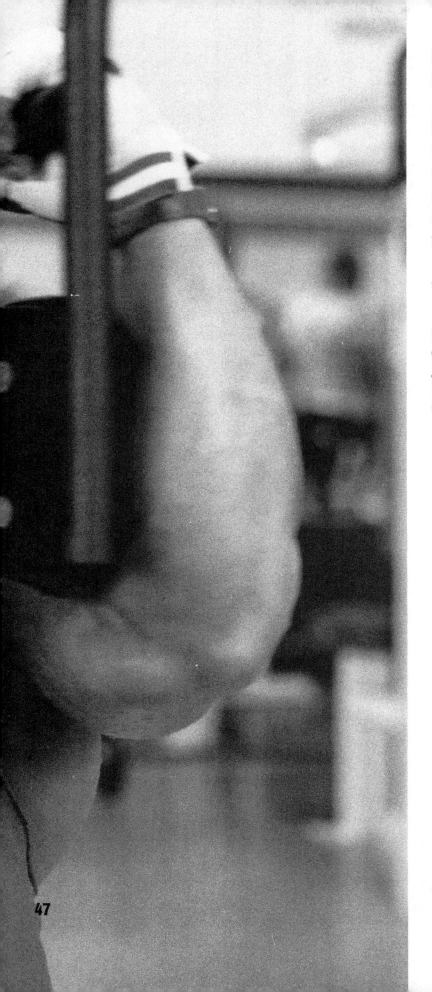

heights of success and creates an ever-growing hunger for more.

Bodybuilding—pushing your body beyond the reasonable bounds of intensity—nurtures this kind of self-esteem, and it is both psychologically rewarding and enduring. It is what champions all feel, and it is what you'll eventually feel.

Bulkbuilding, in my opinion, is what bodybuilding is all about.

Bulkbuilding represents the ultimate limits to which you can push your body, extracting every bit of fiber growth, every bit of strength and power.

Go for it now!

Get big!

BIGGER is BETTER!

Mike Quinn frequently pushes himself beyond the reasonable bounds of intensity. Doing so is necessary for maximum results.

BIG!

CHAPTER 3

SUPER SLOW: THE ULTIMATE FORM OF HIGH-INTENSITY EXERCISE

Super-slow repetitions require much patience and control.

BIG

Another title for this chapter might be *Efficient Muscular Loading*. In a nutshell, efficient muscular loading is what super slow accomplishes better than any other style of exercising. Plus, efficient muscular loading is directly related to getting BIG!

Other styles of training that involve faster speeds of motion, and they all do, load the muscles inconsistently throughout the range of movement, repetition by repetition. What is needed is continuous overloading of the involved muscles in all possible positions. A very slow speed of movement truly permits this to happen.

In training fast, you allow momentum to assist you in lifting the weight. Momentum can help you in a competitive weightlifting contest. In fact, weightlifting is really more weight *throwing* than lifting. But throwing weight hurts you in bodybuilding. Momentum caused by

Exercising in front of a mirror can be helpful in mastering the details of proper form.

fast exercise repeatedly unloads the involved muscles. Unloading muscles detracts from the muscular growth process. The highest-quality loading is required for the highest-quality muscular growth. Quality loading means super slow.

THE IDEAL SPEED OF MOVEMENT

It is now possible to define the lower and upper limits of speed in productive exercise. Using an appropriate resistance with a typical range of movement, the positive phase of this exercise should total a minimum of 6 seconds to avoid meaningful momentum.

At the opposite extreme, a maximum time for most movements would be 15 seconds on the lifting portion. At speeds slower than 15 seconds the movement becomes a series of stops and starts.

Slow movement avoids acceleration effects that erratically load and unload the muscles. The stops and starts of excessively slow movement—15 seconds or longer—introduce a similar result.

From the above discussion a 10-second positive contraction is recommended. It is approximately halfway between the maximum and minimum movement speeds. A 10-second duration is flexible enough to apply to both short- and long-range exercises. And ten is a nice number to work with and to remember.

So, the positive phase of a super-slow repetition is performed in 10 seconds. But what about the negative portion? How many seconds should it require?

Since most trainees are 40 percent stronger in the negative than in the positive, the negative should be done in fewer seconds than the positive.

The recommended guideline is to lower the weight in 5 seconds.

A 5-second negative is followed by a 10-second positive. Thus, the negative is performed at twice the speed of the positive.

SINGLE-JOINT AND MULTIPLE-JOINT EXERCISES

The exercises that I describe in chapter 6 and in chapters 9 through 11 can be grouped in two categories: single-joint and multiple-joint movements. A single-joint exercise—such as the biceps curl, triceps extension, or leg extension—provides movement around one major joint. A multiple-joint exercise—such as the squat, leg press, or bench press—involves movement around two or more joints.

Both single-joint and multiple-joint exercises can be performed using the super-slow protocol. But there is a major difference in their performance. That major difference occurs in the contracted position or upper turnaround. On a single-joint movement, pausing briefly in the contracted position makes the exercise harder and thus more productive.

On a multiple-joint movement just the opposite occurs. The upper turnaround or top position involves a lockout, and locking the joints in a multiple-joint exercise allows you to rest and make the movement easier. So, avoid the lockout position and keep the movement continuous.

Remember, a brief pause is desirable in the upper turnaround of a single-joint movement. But continuous movement is desirable at the upper turnaround of a multiple-joint exercise.

SPECIFIC INSTRUCTIONS

The most complete description of how to perform super-slow exercise comes from Ken Hutchins, the primary architect behind super-slow training. Ken has personally supervised over 10,000 one-on-one, super-slow workouts. The following description of the leg press is from Ken's book *Super Slow: The Ultimate Exercise Protocol*.

To master the super-slow protocol takes considerable understanding, practice, and coaching. You should work through the following exercise with a training partner. Both of you should read carefully the rest of this chapter. Then, have your training partner instruct you through the leg press. Rest a few minutes and do the same for your partner.

Select an appropriate weight on the leg press that permits smooth control. Struggling with a weight that is too heavy permits a series of bad habits. Rather than bad habits, you want to reinforce impeccable form.

The following italicized paragraphs are spoken to you by your training partner or instructor. The bracketed paragraphs offer further explanations.

Bear in mind that learning this first exercise seems tedious initially. But once you master it, you will readily extend the information to the other exercises.

Already, you may be acquainted with the terms "positive work" and "negative work." If so, this will serve somewhat as a review. It's necessary to define these terms to minimize confusion as we proceed.

The weight stack rises as you perform positive work. As it is lowered, you do negative work. Remember that these definitions are determined by the weight stack's direction, not your body's upward or downward direction.

Slowly push the movement arm, almost but not completely straightening your legs and raising the weight stack. As the legs near lockout on the first repetition, stop the subject and explain: Never go any farther toward lockout than right here [knees slightly bent]. *Note that the movement becomes easier at this point. This is due to the muscle unloading as you near lockout. Avoid lockout. Not only might you pop your knees and injure them, but it is wasted motion and time. Since there is no meaningful load at or near lockout, there is no exercise. Once you near lockout and begin to sense easier movement, slowly turnaround and begin the negative phase of the movement.*

Do this a couple more times to get a general idea of the leg press movement.

[Once reaching bottomout again.] *Stop. As you already know, super slow uses a 10-second positive and a 5-second negative. On your next repetition I want you to raise the weight in approximately 10 seconds. Anything between 8 and 12 seconds is acceptable, but aim for 10.*

I will count zero to ten so that you can gauge speed. For two reasons, I do not want you to count—either aloud or silently to yourself. The first reason: You are required to think of four or five factors simultaneously when performing super slow. You cannot maintain attention to these details if you are also counting.

The second reason: See the clock on the wall to your right? Note that its second hand moves in an even, continuous sweep. Excepting neck and head position admonishments momentarily, watch the clock on the opposite wall. Note that its second hand jumps each second interval. Its movement is in segments and is non-continuous. Segmented movements are undesirable. If you count, you will tend to segment rather than produce smooth, continuous movement.

When I count I will say, "zero, one, two, three, four, and you should be halfway, six, seven, eight, nine, ten." Go ahead and perform some repetitions. I will count for you.

[Count for the trainee. Do so as the quotations indicate. Do not say "one-thousand-one, one-thousand-two . . ." This becomes an obnoxious drone to the trainee as well as a laborious mouthful for the instructor. It dries the mouth and fatigues the voice. It also restricts the instructor's flexibility to insert quick comments between the numbers.]

[If you are unsure of cadence speed, check yourself intermittently with a clock or stopwatch.]

[As you should now realize, the instructor is required to do a lot of talking during an introductory workout. To save your voice, restrict words to a minimum.]

[The trainee will invariably fire out of the stretch on his first try. Patiently direct him to start over until he gets it correctly. Emphasize, "You should be halfway." Say it quickly to maintain the correct cadence. Perhaps say, "You should be halfway and you are" to reinforce proper behavior. If performance is poor—especially after several tries—make sure he has an idea of the approximate halfway point. Make sure that he understands that he is not attaining it in the appropriate time. This gives him a starting, middle, and ending position to shoot for.]

[Coax the subject to slowly turnaround and lower the weight.] *Slowly turnaround, lower the weight, and do another.*

[Concentrating to perfect a 10-second positive, the subject invariably performs the negative too slowly. During the negative, encourage him to move faster but without dropping the weight. After several repetitions and at bottomout:] *Stop. Let's talk some more. You're getting better at your positives. Now let's polish your turnarounds and negatives. Do you know what I mean by "turnarounds"?* [Reply from subject.]

A turnaround is the slow but perpetual motion that occurs when changing direction. Again determined by weight-stack position, we speak of the upper turnaround and the lower turnaround.

The upper turnaround begins as you

A slow speed of movement stimulates maximum
involvement of the muscle fibers.

sense unloading just prior to lockout. Begin moving slower, simultaneously changing direction. Try not to completely stop in any position. After moving downward as slowly as possible for a short distance after the stroke peak, begin to gradually accelerate.

Once at that point where you are perceivably accelerating, the upper turnaround is completed. You have entered the body of the negative phase. Continue to accelerate, being careful that acceleration is not excessive. Do not allow a sudden speed increase. Also ensure that speed does not become tantamount to dropping or freefall. Perform the negative at a speed that you feel meaningfully loaded all the way down.

After lowering the weight approximately two-thirds of its stroke, begin to slow down. The body of the negative phase is complete at this point. You have entered the realm of the lower turnaround. Approach the bottom of the stroke slowly enough to avoid slamming into bottomout. Bottomout occurs as the weights—pinned for you to lift—touch the remainder of the weight stack or the frame of the machine. Bottomout may not occur in some exercises, because the machine stroke exceeds your range of motion.

If you are reasonably capable of bottomout, then do so, but without slamming into it. If bottomout is not possi-

The ideal speed of movement requires approximately ten seconds to lift the weight and five seconds to lower it.

56

ble, it remains undesirable to slam into a stretched position of your joints.

Back to the leg press.

Unless your seat position is incorrect, or you have joint or muscular limitations, or you are extremely large, you should lightly bottomout on every repetition. Think "barely touch, barely start." If you avoid bottomout OR unload at bottomout OR fire out of bottomout, your hip muscles are not effectively worked. The first 3 or 4 positive inches of leg press are important. The first inch is most important.

[Often, novices first learn a slow positive, but perform the negative too slowly. Their upper turnaround is naturally quite good.]

[Novices next become preoccupied with the lower turnaround to the point of being careful about the bottomout, but then lose control by inadvertently firing out of the stretch. With practice during their first workout, this corrects. The remaining discrepancy is the too-slow negative phase.]

[Do not count a cadence for every repetition. Count one, coax one, count one, coax two or three, count one.]

[An example of coaxing repetition:] *Barely squeeze out of the start, then slow down . . . Keep it barely moving . . . Don't let it stop . . .* [If you anticipate a lunge or you can see that the subject is increasing speed inappropriately] *hold back . . .* [near the top]. *Carefully turnaround . . . Ease out of the top position . . . Gradually increase speed . . . faster . . . faster . . . faster . . .* [two-thirds way down]. *Slower . . .* [One inch from the bottom] *barely touch, barely start . . . Once you get it barely going, keep it barely going.* [Repeat.]

[During counting or coaxing, speak softly but with enough volume to be heard. The subject startles if you bark at him.]

[One immediate need for an <u>instructional insert</u> during a cadence count is to remind the novice to breathe. You appreciate instructional inserts especially when teaching more complex exercises. For example, try simultaneous counting, coaxing, and correcting pullover discrepancies. To explain the entire cycle of repetition, note the schematic on page 59. Draw it for your novice to graphically represent desired superslow performance.]

A complete repetition cycle is represented by this continuous loop. The <u>entire positive</u> is the distance from the bottomout point to the stroke peak. The <u>body of the positive</u> is the solid upward arrow. The <u>body of the negative</u> is the solid downward arrow. The dashed line is the <u>realm of the upper turnaround</u>. The dotted line is the <u>realm of the lower turnaround</u>.

It is natural and expected that your negatives are too slow. Once you slow down, you naturally slow down everything. To help you to increase speed a little, I will count cadence during the negative.

Once your direction changes after the stroke peak, begin to gradually accelerate. I will begin counting from "zero" at that point where your acceleration should begin. I will count, "zero, one, two, three, four, zero." On "zero" you should be starting the repetition. This 5-second interval includes the entire body of the negative, plus the deceleration and gentle bottomout of the lower turnaround. [Point these out on the schematic as you talk.]

SCHEMATIC CYCLE

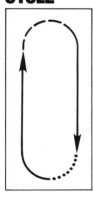

The body of the negative is the only movement range where you can significantly increase speed. In super slow you perform positives in 10 seconds. You cannot increase speed during the upper or lower turnaround. [Point these out as you talk.]

Back to work. Let's rehearse some more repetitions. By the way, I will not routinely count cadence. I expect you to gain a feel for the proper speed during each exercise. In the event that I sense that your speed is incorrect, I will count cadence once or twice so that you can adjust. Carry on.

[Allow the subject to perform eight or nine repetitions consecutively. Alternately count, one, etc. It might help to count several repetitions in tandem. Example: "zero, one, two, three, four, five, six, seven, eight, nine, ten. Pause for upper turnaround. Then just after the upper turnaround: Zero, one, two, three, four, zero, one, two . . . ten." Also try: "zero, one . . . four, you should be starting the next one, two . . . ten." Say that last phrase at the speed allowing "starting" to fall exactly on "zero" and allowing "one" to fall exactly on "one" of the next series. It should occupy a duration of two seconds—from "four" to "one." "Zero" is, of course, omitted.]

[Miscellaneous advice: Cadence counting is often required for the novice. Once the subject is moderately proficient, cadence counting is rarely needed. Furthermore, it becomes a nuisance and an unnecessary distraction. You do not want the subject to depend on its use.]

[Once mastery of the first exercise is attained, a few additional exercises are often quickly assimilated. For the most part, this occurs with little if any cadence counting for the remainder of the introductory workout.]

[Hand signals: It is difficult both to cadence count AND coax the novice to accelerate on the same negative. With your hands in his line of sight, communicate your instructions to increase speed

The upright row with a barbell is a great exercise for the shoulders and upper back.

by twirling your index finger. If the meaning of this is agreed upon with the novice, coaxing and counting are simultaneously possible. Devise other signals if appropriate, but do not distract him from proper head and neck position.]

Thanks again to Ken Hutchins for permission to reprint the preceding instructions from his book *Super Slow: The Ultimate Exercise Protocol*. To order a copy of this book, send a check or money order for $26.50 to Media Support, P.O. Box 180154, Casselberry, FL 32718-0154.

REINFORCEMENT FROM THE PAST

From 1963 to 1967 I was a student at Baylor University in Waco, Texas. During this time I frequently entered bodybuilding and powerlifting contests throughout Texas. Dallas was a hotbed for training, and the strongest lifter in Dallas was Ronnie Ray.

Ronnie's workouts were unique. Most of his training repetitions and maximum attempts were performed in the absolutely strictest style. And his specialty, the bench press, was practiced in a super-slow form.

We all thought Ronnie was crazy to perform his lifts in such a slow manner. He could have easily bench pressed 10 or 15 percent more weight with a faster speed of motion. As a result, no one copied Ronnie's training. It was too much of a letdown to reduce your train-

ing poundage significantly to do so.

For the record, however, lifting slowly and strictly worked beautifully for Ronnie. During the late 1960s he held the American bench press record in three weight classes simultaneously.

I never bothered to ask Ronnie how he devised his training philosophy until recently. In 1988 I spent an afternoon showing Ronnie around the Nautilus Research Center in Dallas. He noted that he was lifting hard again and was entering the Master's competition soon. In fact, in his last workout he had performed three repetitions in the bench press with 440 pounds, in strict super-slow style.

"How did you get the idea of training slowly?" I asked Ronnie.

"I borrowed the slow training from Pat Casey and Bill West, two Californian powerlifters, around 1963," Ronnie replied. "I was suffering from my usual shoulder pain and normal bench pressing was extremely painful. As the guys from the West Coast suggested, I found slow positives very productive and safe for my shoulders."

So, super slow was used successfully by a few powerlifters over twenty-five years ago. But it certainly wasn't appreciated and utilized as it should have been.

Properly applied, super slow is the ultimate form of high-intensity exercise.

A variation of the upright row can be performed with a cable attachment.

Eddie Robinson has experienced the effects of super-slow exercise.

BIG!

CHAPTER 4
SUPER-SLOW PRINCIPLES

BIG

A slow speed of movement is necessary for maximum muscular contraction.

"More important than lifting a weight," Ken Hutchins says, "is how you lift it. More important than how you lift a weight is how you attempt to lift it once lifting becomes nearly or totally impossible."

The most productive part of the exercise, according to Ken, occurs after positive muscular failure. When you are unable to continue the super-slow leg press as described in the last chapter, do *not* lower the weight and exit the machine. Keep pressing into the contraction— breathe, concentrate, visualize it moving—and maybe you will get a couple more inches of movement. The idea is to press or try to lift the weight for a good 15 seconds once perceptible movement stops. This makes a deeper inroad into the growth stimulation process.

Besides impeccable form, slow

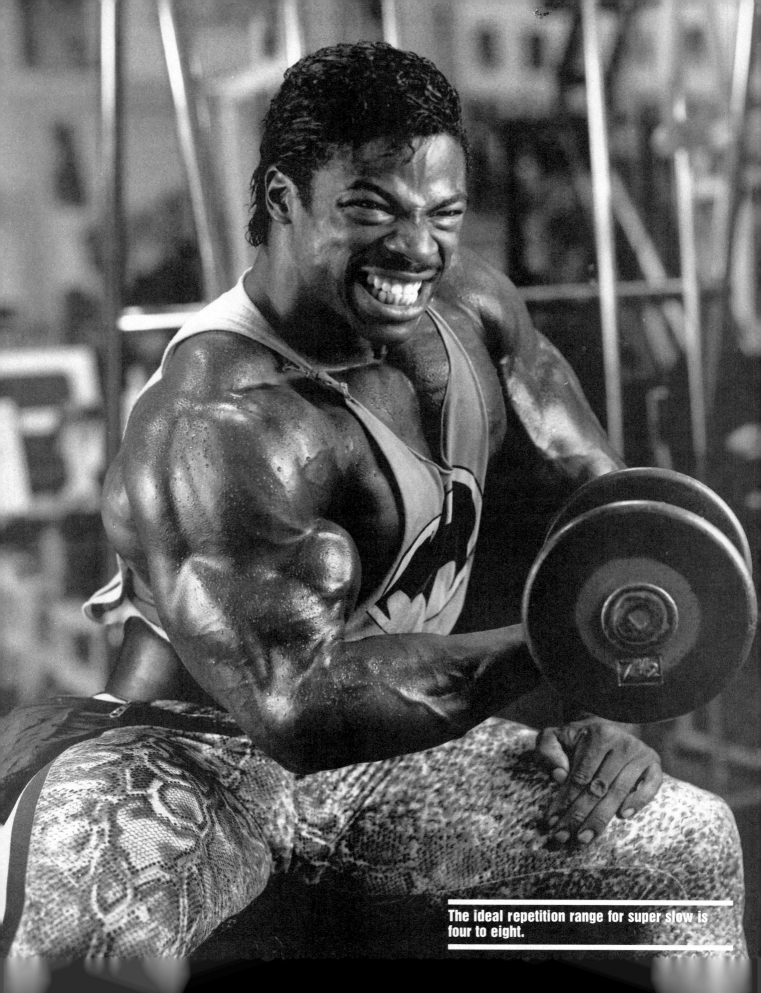

The ideal repetition range for super slow is four to eight.

For high degrees of cardiovascular involvement it is important to move quickly from one exercise to the next.

Scott Wilson performs the last repetition of cable rows with great intensity, while Shane DiMora seems to be implying that "Such exercise is a piece of cake."

"Now it's your turn," Scott says to Shane. Super slow is anything but a piece of cake. It must be experienced to be fully appreciated.

speed of movement, and the final contraction past failure, other high-intensity rules are instrumental to building massive muscles. Let's examine each one in detail.

HOW MANY REPETITIONS?

Each super-slow repetition requires approximately 15 seconds to complete. Experience shows that momentary muscular failure on each exercise should occur between 60 and 120 seconds. Thus, the ideal repetition range for super slow is four to eight.

Always do as many repetitions in good form as you can, regardless of the number. When you perform eight or more, however, that is the signal to increase the resistance by 5 percent at the next workout. A 5-percent increase in the weight will reduce your repetitions to the lower end of the range.

HOW MANY EXERCISES?

Each exercise that you perform makes an inroad into your starting level of strength. If a fresh muscle's maximum-force output is 100 pounds and the same muscle's fatigued strength is 75 pounds, then the inroad from the involved exercise is 25 percent.

Evidently, some chemical thresh-old is crossed when a weakened muscle attempts a momentarily impossible movement. The body reads this as meaningful inroad/intensity and the involved muscles are stimulated to grow larger and stronger. The growth process actually occurs later: usually 36 to 48 hours after the stimulation. Maximum growth, however, will not occur unless the targeted muscles and the system as a whole are well rested.

A well-rested body is dependent primarily on the briefness of your workout. Generally speaking, the less time you spend training for the desired stimulation, the better. This is especially true with super-slow exercise since it makes a deeper inroad into your recovery ability.

Experience shows that the maximum number of exercises you should do is twelve. In many cases, you'll get even better results by doing no more than ten exercises per workout.

Eddie Mueller's workouts, which are described in Part II, consisted of only ten exercises. Sometimes he did two sets of a movement, but each set was counted as one of the ten exercises. None of his workouts ever lasted longer than 30 minutes.

For maximum growth stimulation, keep your exercises to twelve or fewer and your workouts to 30 minutes or less.

Seated calf raise:
Try to stand on your
big toes.

Super-slow, seated calf raises will make your lower legs ache clear to the bone.

HOW MANY WORKOUTS PER WEEK?

Your body needs at least 48 hours, but not more than 96 hours, of rest between high-intensity workouts. Training your entire body on Monday, Wednesday, and Friday, with rest and recovery on the in-between days, is the recommended schedule. Thus, you have approximately 48 hours of elapsed time after the Monday and Wednesday workouts, and 72 hours after the Friday session. The extra 24 hours of recovery time on the weekend is helpful and adds a bit of needed irregularity to the overall schedule.

KEEPING ACCURATE RECORDS

Many bodybuilders avoid keeping track of what they do during their training sessions. Instead, they work for a feel or a pump. This is a mistake.

There is a direct correlation between the size of a muscle and the strength of a muscle. Increasing one increases the other. Furthermore, it is easier to measure the strength of a muscle than its size.

The strength of a muscle is best measured not by seeing how much you can lift at one time maximally, but by observing how much you can

lift for several repetitions. With the super-slow protocol, five repetitions is a good guideline to follow for comparisons. Thus, by comparing your five-repetition sets for the same exercise to one another, you should be able to calculate your percent increases on a weekly and monthly basis.

Be sure to keep an accurate training record of all your workouts. This can be done on a card that lists the exercises with ample space to the right for recording the date, order, resistance, repetitions, and training time.

SUPER-SLOW TRAINING RULES

The following principles summarize chapters 3 and 4 and form the basis of the most effective and efficient way to bulk your body: The High-Intensity, Super-Slow Training System.

- Select a weight for each exercise that allows performance of between four and eight super-slow repetitions.
- Lift the resistance on each repetition slowly in 10 seconds. Lower the resistance smoothly in 5 seconds.
- Concentrate on performing slow, deliberate turnarounds at each end of the movement. Emphasize

a brief pause in the upper turn-around of a single-joint exercise. Stress continuous movement at the upper turnaround of a multiple-joint exercise.

- Do *not* hold your breath during any super-slow repetition. Keep your mouth open and emphasize breathing out.
- Continue each exercise until momentary muscular failure. At failure, keep exerting force against the resistance for another 15 seconds.
- Increase the resistance by 5 percent at the next workout when you can perform eight or more repetitions in good form.
- Attempt constantly to increase the number of repetitions or the amount of weight, or both. But do not sacrifice form in an attempt to increase your repetitions or weight.
- Perform no more than a total of twelve sets of all exercises in any one super-slow session.
- Train no more than three times a week.
- Keep accurate records—date, order, resistance, repetitions, and overall training time—of each workout.

Lying triceps extension: Concentrate on performing slow, deliberate turnarounds at each end of the movement.

BIG!

CHAPTER 5
BULKBUILDING AND RECUPERATION

Massive muscular growth requires a well-rested recovery ability.

BIG

Without rest and relaxation your body cannot overcompensate between workouts.

There are at least four keys to building awesome muscular bulk and great physical power: exercise, diet, psychological factors, and optimum recuperation between workouts. Of these four requirements, recuperation is the least understood, least frequently monitored, and can be the most important in your quest for getting big.

Your muscles require sufficient rest to recuperate fully from a high-intensity workout. They will not grow in response to that workout until they have fully recovered from it. It is essential that you take steps to foster full recuperation between workouts because you won't make progress from your training unless you do recover completely in between.

Your body is a dynamic energy system. Every hour that you live and breathe, you are burning energy and replenishing energy. In many ways this dynamic energy system is like your

Rich Gaspari knows how easy it is to overtrain.

bank account, in which you constantly make deposits and withdrawals. When you withdraw more money than you have deposited, you go broke—you've overdrawn. When you use more energy than you can replenish, you go energy broke—you've overtrained.

Overtraining is the greatest obstacle to progress that a bodybuilder can face. When you are overtrained, you will either progress at a very slow pace, or you'll no longer be able to face going to the gym to work out. In some cases, you can actually lose muscular size and strength.

It's easy to avoid overtraining, if you know how. Normally, you will overtrain when you allow your workouts to become too long rather than too hard. As long as you are exercising with great intensity, you won't overtrain, because a demanding workout is by definition a relatively short training session. You won't be able to train efficiently for more than 45 minutes when you are pushing as hard as you can in a workout. Many times, 30 minutes will be all you can stand.

COMMON SYMPTOMS OF OVERTRAINING

Below you will find listed the ten most common symptoms of an impending overtrained state. If you notice two or more of these symptoms, you are probably on the verge of overtraining.

- Persistent lack of energy
- Constantly sore joints and muscles
- Elevated waking pulse rate
- Elevated morning blood pressure
- Irritability
- Insomnia
- Loss of appetite
- Headaches
- Lack of enthusiasm for workouts
- Injury and/or illness

The following true story is an excellent example of overtraining. I first mentioned it in my book *Big Arms in Six Weeks*, and I'd like to rehash it again.

BUILDING MUSCLE BY RESTING

"Gee! I can't believe it," said Mark, a twenty-one-year-old bodybuilder-athlete. "I haven't worked out a single time in four weeks and my arms are one-eighth of an inch bigger."

It was at midpoint of my *Big Arms in Six Weeks* program, and I was measuring the arms of the participants. Eric was up ⅝ of an inch, Kenny showed a ⅜-inch improvement, and Corrine noted an increase of ½ inch. Most of the others were up at least ¼ of an inch. I purposely measured Mark's arm last.

Mark, usually known as "Mr. Enthusiasm," had been going through some tough times. He had done a lot of busy-work for me organizing the course, in which he was going to be one of the participants. But several days before the program was to begin, Mark seriously injured his eye while hammering a nail

Heavy-duty, high-intensity workouts must be brief in duration.

into a board. He had not hit the nail squarely, and it ricocheted off the board and the flat end punctured his eye.

The doctor told him in no uncertain terms that if he wanted to have normal functions of his left eye again, it would mean almost complete rest for eight to ten weeks. Absolutely no exercise was permitted, not even calisthenics. And especially no heavy-resistance training or strenuous lifting. The least bit of vigorous activity might place too much stress on the delicate inner-eye tissues. His eye could be damaged permanently.

At least a half-dozen times Mark had asked me, "Dr. Darden, if I don't exercise for eight weeks, what's going to happen to my body?"

"You'll probably lose ten pounds of muscle mass quickly—within two weeks," I replied, judging from my past experience of working with injured athletes.

"Isn't there anything I can do to prevent this from happening?" Mark questioned.

"No," I replied. "Just do exactly what your doctor says—and be patient. As soon as your eye has healed and you start training again, you'll quickly regain your lost muscle mass."

After four weeks of zero training on Mark's part, I was expecting to measure his arms and see a loss of ¼ to ½ inch. When the tape registered an increase of ⅛ of an inch, I stopped, took the tape away, checked it for accuracy, and remeasured. Again the same ⅛-inch gain.

"What's happened to your body weight, Mark?" I asked.

"I've put on a few pounds," he replied.

"Something doesn't make sense," I thought to myself, as I walked over to the water fountain to get a drink.

When I returned, Mark was deep in thought. "Dr. Darden," he said as he glanced up at me, "you don't suppose that all these years I've been overtraining?"

Then, as if lightning had flashed through the roof, I started to picture what was happening.

TOO MUCH ACTIVITY

"Mark, before your eye injury," I asked, "what was your typical day like? Give me a rundown on all your activities."

He recited a litany, telling me how he began with fifty push-ups and sit-ups each morning, with a repeat of the ritual before turning in at night. Three mornings a week he ran one mile, then quickly showered and ate breakfast before riding his ten-speed bicycle to his college classes a couple of miles away. Late in the afternoon he'd play intramural sports: touch football, basketball, and softball.

As a floor manager at the Gainesville Health and Fitness Center, Mark used the club's facilities for four upper-body workouts per week.

He wasn't finished reciting, but I'd heard all I could stand.

"Sorry to interrupt, Mark," I said, "but you've listed enough already. There's no doubt in my mind. Yes! You've been overtraining. Not by a little, but by a bunch.

"During the last four weeks, even though you had a serious eye injury, your body—for perhaps the first time in years—had the time to rest, recover, overcompensate, and grow. And it did—as evidenced by the one-eighth-inch improvement in the size of your arm and the gain you've noted in your body weight. We can now all profit from your unfortunate but meaningful experience."

TAKE A WEEK OFF

If you feel as though your body, like Mark's, is in a state of overtraining, combat the situation by first taking a week off from training. When you return to the gym, be sure that you increase the intensity of your workouts and decrease the length to avoid future overtraining.

To maintain a positive energy balance, you must avoid energy leaks. Primarily, these energy leaks result from being uptight about some area of your life. You might not consider a nervous energy leak of much magnitude, but it can be considerable. You can actually burn up more energy in one psycho-

Your body grows when you're resting, not when you're exercising. Always allow plenty of time between workouts for rest and contentment.

logically bad day than you can expend in a high-intensity workout.

Be careful to maintain a tranquil mind at all times. Sometimes this isn't easy to do, but you can greatly improve your state of mind by learning how to combat stress in your daily life. A good book on this subject is *Unlimited Power* by Anthony Robbins.

It is equally important to plug unnecessary physical-energy leaks. It's not a good practice to engage in any other physical sport or intense activity that draws energy from the bulkbuilding routine. Take a good look at individuals who run five miles per day and you'll see that they have little muscle mass, an indication of what can happen to your physique if you do too much aerobic activity and overtrain. Your energy while on a bulk-building routine should be conserved and utilized primarily for the building of mass.

BUILDING ENERGY RESERVES

You should also build up your energy reserves. The main way to do this is to allow your body sufficient sleep and rest to permit full recovery between training sessions. It's in your sleeping hours that your body is rebuilding and creating energy and muscular size. That's why sleep and relaxation are so important. Individual sleep requirements vary widely, so you need to experiment with a variety of sleep schedules to determine what is best for you. Take 8 hours as an average amount of sleep and experiment from that starting point.

Proper rest throughout the day can also influence your recuperative abilities. Perhaps you should take a nap in the late afternoon if you feel the need.

An optimum bodybuilding diet is a very important aspect of energy production. Such a diet will be discussed in detail in the next chapter.

If you take the correct energy-conservation measures and the right steps to replenish spent energy, you will recover optimally from your workouts and make better gains in your bulkbuilding.

BIG!

CHAPTER 6
THE BEST BULKBUILDING EXERCISES

Lee Haney performs the incline press with a barbell.

Naturally, there are some exercises that are better than others for building mass and bulk. All the best ones will be listed and described in this chapter.

A key factor in bulkbuilding, however, is not the exercise as much as it is the way you do the movement. I hope you're convinced by now that a super-slow style of performance is the best way to stimulate your muscles to grow.

Here's a complete list of all the exercises, according to body part, that are described in this chapter.

BULKBUILDING EXERCISES

THIGHS
- Squat with barbell
- Leg extension
- Leg press
- Leg curl

CALVES
- Standing calf raise
- Donkey calf raise

SHOULDERS
- Lateral raise with dumbbells
- Press behind neck with barbell
- Upright row with barbell

BACK
- Bent-over row with barbell
- Straight-armed pullover with one dumbbell
- Bent-armed pullover with barbell
- Lat machine pulldown
- Shoulder shrug with barbell
- Stiff-legged deadlift with barbell

CHEST
- Bent-armed fly with dumbbells
- Bench press with barbell
- Decline press to neck with barbell

BICEPS
- Biceps curl with barbell
- Biceps curl with dumbbells
- Reverse curl with barbell
- Chin-up
- Negative chin-up

TRICEPS
- Triceps extension with one dumbbell
- Dip
- Negative dip

FOREARMS
- Wrist curl with barbell
- Reverse wrist curl with barbell

MIDSECTION
- Trunk curl
- Reverse trunk curl

The incline press involves the triceps, front deltoids, and pectorals.

THIGHS
Squat with Barbell

Emphasis: The squat is the single best bulkbuilding exercise. It stresses primarily the buttocks, quadriceps, hamstrings, and lower back muscles. Secondary emphasis is placed on the upper back, calves, and abdominal muscle groups. Regular squatting will make your body's metabolism more conducive to adding bulk all over your physique, not just in your legs.

Starting position: Place a barbell on a squat rack and load it with an appropriate amount of weight. Remember, with the super-slow style you'll need 30 to 40 percent less resistance than you normally use for ten repetitions. Position the bar behind your neck across your trapezius muscles and hold the bar in place with your hands. If the bar cuts into your skin, pad it lightly by wrapping a towel around the knurl.

Straighten your legs to lift the bar off the rack and move back one step. Place your feet shoulder-width apart, toes angled slightly outward. Keep your upper body muscles rigid and your torso upright during the exercise. It also helps if you focus on a spot on the wall at eye level as you do the movement.

Movement: Bend your hips and knees and smoothly descend to a position whereby your hamstrings firmly come in contact with your calves. Without bouncing, or without stopping in the bottom position, slowly make the turnaround from negative to positive. Take 10 seconds to lift the barbell back almost to the top position. Do not lock your legs. Keep a bend of approximately 15 degrees in your knees. Repeat the 5-second lowering and 10-second lifting for maximum repetitions.

Training tips: It's important that you don't allow your torso to bend forward as you rise out of the bottom position. You'll find it easier to perform a repetition with this cheating technique, but it takes stress from your thighs and places potentially harmful force on your lower back. As a safety measure, it is also a good idea to use spotters during the squat.

Leg Extension

Emphasis: The leg extension, which is available on many types of leg extension machines, is the best isolation movement for your quadriceps.

Starting position: Sit in the machine and place your feet behind the bottom roller pads. If possible, align the axis of rotation of the movement arm with your knees. If a belt is provided, strap it tightly across your hips to keep your buttocks from rising. Lean back and stabilize your upper body by grasping the side of the machine.

Movement: Straighten your legs very slowly in 10 seconds. Ease into the fully contracted top position. Pause briefly. Lower the weight smoothly in 5 seconds. Repeat the 10-second lifting and 5-second lowering for maximum repetitions.

Most of the basic barbell exercises can be performed with dumbbells.

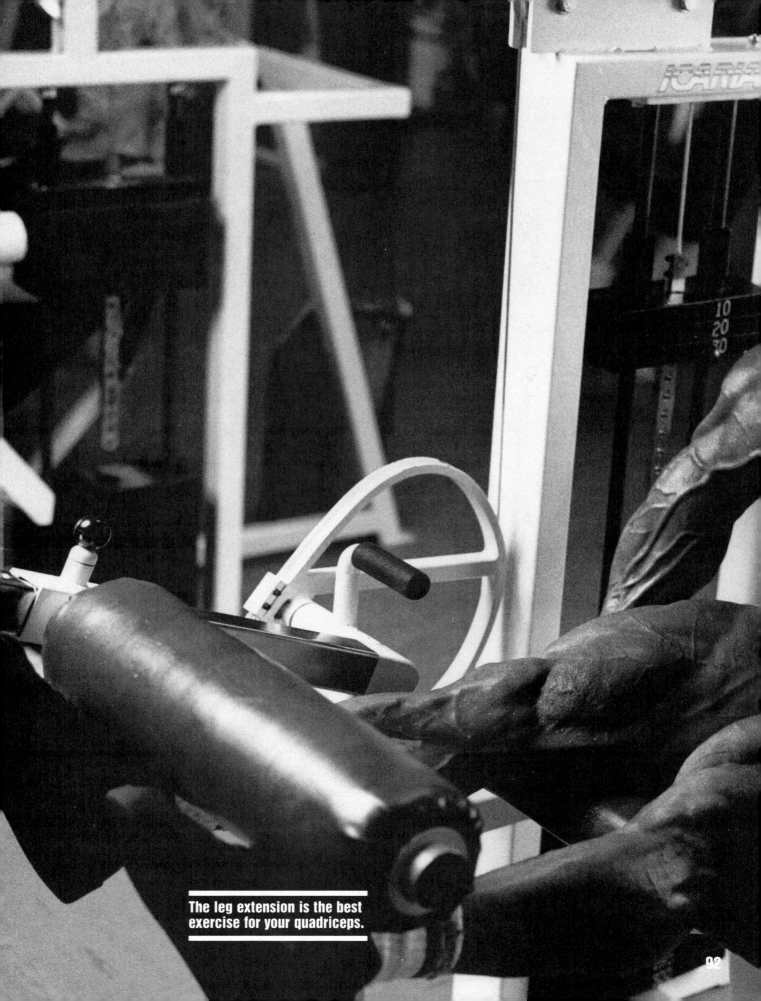

The leg extension is the best exercise for your quadriceps.

Training tips: Relax your feet during the movement. Do not point your toes or flex them. Keep your neck relaxed as well. Do not move your head forward or side to side. On the last repetitions, emphasize your breathing. Do not hold your breath. Stress smooth turnarounds at both ends of the exercise.

Leg Press

Emphasis: An alternative to the squat is the leg press, which can be performed on a wide variety of machines. The leg press involves the quadriceps, hamstrings, and buttocks intensively, but places less stress on the rest of the body than squats.

Starting position: Sit in the machine with your back against the angled pad and your buttocks on the seat bottom. Place your feet on the movable platform with your heels about shoulder-width apart and your toes pointed slightly outward. Straighten your legs and release the stop bars of the machine (be sure to lock these stop bars at the end of your set to secure the platform). Grasp the handles beside the seat or the edge of the seat during the movement.

Movement: From the top position, lower the weight in 5 seconds. Bring your knees to the sides of your chest and smoothly make the turnaround from negative to positive. Raise the weight slowly in 10 seconds. Do not let your legs lockout. Keep a bend of 15 degrees in your knees. Repeat the 5-second lowering and 10-second lifting for maximum repetitions.

Training tips: Practice smooth turnarounds at both the top and the bottom. Do not slam into the platform or bounce and bang the resistance at either end of the exercise.

Leg Curl

Emphasis: The leg curl is to your hamstrings or back thighs what the leg extension is to your quadriceps. Many companies manufacture leg curl machines and most of them function in a similar manner.

Starting position: Lie facedown on the leg curl machine with your knees on the pad edge closest to the movement arm. Hook your heels under the roller pads. Make certain your knees are in line with the axis of rotation of the machine. Grasp the handles provided on the edges of the machine bench to steady your upper body.

Movement: Curl your heels slowly in 10 seconds and try to touch the roller pads to your buttocks. Near the fully contracted position, you must lift your buttocks off the pad and slightly arch your back. Do *not* try to keep your hips down. Pause briefly in the top position. Ease out of the top position and lower the movement arm in 5 seconds. Repeat the 10-second lifting and 5-second lowering for maximum repetitions.

Training tips: Keep your feet relaxed during the first half of each repetition. As you move into the last half, or the contracted position, move your toes toward your knees. This dorsi flexing of your feet stretches your back calves and allows for a greater range of motion from the hamstrings.

CALVES
Standing Calf Raise

Emphasis: This is the standard exercise for building your gastrocnemius or back calf muscles. It can be performed on a variety of machines.

Starting position: Face the machine and bend your knees enough so you can position your shoulders beneath the yoke of the machine. Stand and place your feet shoulder-width apart on the toe block or step, with only your toes and the balls of your feet in contact with the block. Straighten your knees and keep them locked throughout the exercise. Sag your heels as far below the level of your toes as comfortably possible. Keep your feet pointed straight ahead.

Movement: Raise your heels slowly in 10 seconds and try to stand on your tiptoes. Do not bend your knees. Pause briefly in the highest position. Lower smoothly to the bottom and stretch. Repeat the 10-second raising and 5-second lowering for maximum repetitions.

Training tips: Many bodybuilders are convinced that turning their toes in during calf raises works more of the lateral head of the gastrocnemius. Likewise, turning the toes out involves more of the medial head. Such techniques, however, are unfounded since the origin and insertion points of the gastrocnemius are not altered by foot placement. Varying your foot position does add variety to a generally boring exercise, and there's no harm in doing so.

Donkey Calf Raise

Emphasis: The donkey calf raise is a favorite of mine because it allows for better concentration, and better isolation, of the gastrocnemius muscles. Although this exercise can be done on several different machines, the style preferred by most trainers is with a partner astride the hips.

Starting position: Place the balls of your feet on a sturdy block of wood that's at least 4 inches thick. Bend over and lean against a chair or bench. Your back should be parallel with the floor. Your partner then sits across your hips as if he were riding a donkey. Lock your knees and keep them locked throughout the exercise. Drop your heels to a comfortable stretch.

Movement: Raise your heels slowly in 10 seconds, stand on your tiptoes, and contract your calves intensely. In the top position, try to stand on your big toes. Lower your heels smoothly in 5 seconds. Stretch at the bottom by extending and spreading your toes. This will force your heels lower. Repeat the 10-second raising and the 5-second lowering for maximum repetitions.

Training tips: You'll receive the full force of your training partner's body weight if you make certain he positions himself well back on your hips. His torso should also remain upright, as opposed to leaning forward.

SHOULDERS
Lateral Raise with Dumbbells

Emphasis: This is the best exercise to add beef to your medial deltoids. It can be performed seated or standing.

Starting position: Grasp a dumbbell in each hand and stand. Lock your elbows and wrists and keep them locked throughout the exercise. All the action should occur around your shoulder joints.

Movement: Raise your arms sideways slowly in 10 seconds. Pause briefly when the dumbbells are slightly above the horizontal. Make sure your palms are facing down and your elbows are straight. Lower smoothly to your sides in 5 seconds. Repeat the 10-second raising and 5-second lowering for maximum repetitions.

Training tips: Resist the temptation to cheat on this exercise by leaning forward, bringing the dumbbells together, and using momentum to initiate the movement at the bottom.

Press Behind Neck with Barbell

Emphasis: This exercise works your deltoids and triceps.

Starting position: In a standing position, place the barbell behind your neck. Your hands should be 3 inches wider on each side than your shoulders.

Movement: Press the barbell over-

The squat is the single best bulkbuilding exercise you can do with a barbell.

head slowly in 10 seconds. Do not lock-out your elbows. Keep a slight bend in them at the top. Lower the barbell smoothly in 5 seconds behind your neck. Repeat the 10-second pressing and 5-second lowering for maximum repetitions.

Training tips: Do not bounce the barbell off your shoulders at the bottom. Emphasize the bottom turnaround by keeping the movement smooth and steady.

Upright Row with Barbell

Emphasis: The upright row involves the deltoids and trapezius muscles.

Starting position: Grasp a barbell with a narrow overhanded grip and stand. There should be 6 inches of space between your index fingers, and the barbell should be resting by your upper thighs.

Movement: Pull the barbell upward along the front of your body slowly in 10 seconds until your hands almost touch your neck. Make sure your elbows stay above your hands. Lower the bar smoothly in 5 seconds back to your thighs. Repeat the 10-second raising and the 5-second lowering for maximum repetitions.

Training tips: Keep your torso erect during the movement. Do not lean forward or backward. This allows more work to be placed directly on your shoulders and upper back.

BACK
Bent-over Row with Barbell

Emphasis: The bent-over row stresses primarily the latissimus dorsi and biceps.

Starting position: A variety of hand spacings and grips are possible on this exercise. I recommend a narrow, under-handed grip most of the time. In a bent-over position place your hands 4 inches apart. Your torso should remain parallel to the floor during the movement.

Movement: Pull the barbell up your thighs slowly in 10 seconds until it touches your waist. Lower smoothly in 5 seconds back to the stretched position. Repeat the 10-second raising and 5-second lowering for maximum repetitions.

Training tips: Keep a slight bend in your knees during this movement to reduce the stress on your lower back.

Straight-armed Pullover with One Dumbbell

Emphasis: The straight-armed pullover is great for working your latissimus dorsi muscles, as well as expanding your rib cage.

Starting position: Lie crossways on a bench with your shoulders in contact with the bench and your head and lower body relaxed and off the bench. Hold a dumbbell on one end in both hands and position it over your chest with your arms straight.

Movement: Take a deep breath and lower the dumbbell smoothly in 5 seconds behind your head. Stretch and raise the dumbbell slowly in 10 seconds to the over-chest position. Repeat the 5-second lowering and 10-second raising for maximum repetitions.

Training tips: The emphasis in this exercise is on the stretching that occurs in the bottom position. Stretching is stressed more so when your arms are straight. With a heavy weight you'll probably have to bend your arms. Lighten the resistance and practice stretching with your arms straight. You'll feel the effect much more in your rib cage.

Bent-armed Pullover with Barbell

Emphasis: Because a much heavier weight can be used on the bent-armed pullover compared to the straight-armed version, the emphasis is on the latissimus dorsi more than the rib cage.

Starting position: Lie on a high, narrow bench with your head barely off the edge. Anchor your feet securely underneath. Have a spotter hand you a heavy barbell. Your hands should be spaced 12 inches apart. The barbell should be resting on your chest.

Movement: Move the barbell over your face and head and smoothly try to touch the floor in 5 seconds. Don't straighten your arms; keep them bent. Stretch in the bottom position and slowly pull the barbell in 10 seconds above your face to your chest. Repeat the 5-second lowering and 10-second raising for maximum repetitions.

Training tips: This is a difficult exercise to perform in the super-slow style. If you have access to a Nautilus pullover machine, use it instead. You'll get much better results using the super-slow protocol.

Lat Machine Pulldown

Emphasis: There are a number of different ways to do a lat machine pulldown. The one that stresses your latissimus dorsi muscles the most involves a parallel grip. If a parallel grip bar is not available, use an underhanded grip.

Starting position: Stabilize yourself under the lat machine bar. Grasp the overhead bar with an underhanded grip.

Movement: Pull the bar slowly in 10 seconds to your chest. Return smoothly in 5 seconds to the stretched position. Repeat the 10-second pulling and 5-second lowering for maximum repetitions.

Training tips: As a variation to this exercise, pull the bar behind your neck. The behind-neck version can be done with an underhanded or overhanded grip, or with your hands wide apart or shoulder-width apart.

Shoulder Shrug with Barbell

Emphasis: This exercise directly involves the trapezius muscles of your upper back.

Starting position: Take an overhanded grip on a barbell and stand erect. Your hands should be slightly wider apart than your shoulders, and the bar should be resting against your thighs. Sag your

The leg press can be substituted for the squat.

Leg extension: Always come to a complete stop in
the top position of this exercise.

shoulders forward and downward as far as comfortably possible.

Movement: Shrug your shoulders upward and backward slowly in 10 seconds as high as possible. Pause briefly at the top. Lower smoothly in 5 seconds to the stretched position. Repeat the 10-second shrugging and 5-second lowering for maximum repetitions.

Training tips: When shrugging, keep your arms straight. Bending your arms brings your biceps into action. If your grip starts tiring before your trapezius muscles, use gloves or wrist straps.

Stiff-legged Deadlift with Barbell

Emphasis: This exercise involves your lower back, buttocks, and hamstrings.

Starting position: Even though this exercise is called a stiff-legged deadlift, it should be performed with a slight bend in your knees. This protects the vertebrae of your lower back. Place a small platform underneath the barbell to elevate your feet for a greater range of movement. Stand on the platform and grasp the barbell with one hand under and the other hand over. Your feet should be under the bar. Bend your knees and stand with the barbell.

Movement: Lower the barbell smoothly in 5 seconds down your thighs. Keep a slight bend in your knees throughout the movement. Stretch in the bottom position. Lift the weight slowly in 10 seconds back to an almost erect position. Repeat the 5-second lowering

and 10-second lifting for maximum repetitions.

Training tip: Ease into the stiff-legged deadlift, especially if you have any problem or tenderness in your lower back. For the first several weeks, use a light weight and do not go to momentary muscular failure.

CHEST
Bent-armed Fly with Dumbbells

Emphasis: The bent-armed fly isolates your pectoralis majors, the largest muscles in your chest.

Starting position: Grasp two dumbbells, lie back on a flat exercise bench, and extend your arms upward from your shoulders. Your palms should be facing each other while holding the dumbbells. Bend your elbows slightly and keep them bent throughout the movement.

Movement: Lower the dumbbells smoothly in 5 seconds out to the sides in semicircular arcs as low as comfortably possible. Return the dumbbells slowly in 10 seconds along the same arcs to the top position. Repeat the 5-second lowering and 10-second lifting for maximum repetitions.

Training tips: In the stretched position, when viewed from the side, it is important to keep your hands, elbows, and shoulders in line with one another. This directs most of the emphasis on your chest muscles.

Leg curl: Slow, smooth repetitions will quickly fatigue your hamstrings.

Bench Press with Barbell

Emphasis: A favorite exercise of many bodybuilders, the bench press stresses your pectorals, deltoids, and triceps.

Starting position: Load a barbell resting on the rack at the head end of a flat exercise bench. Lie on the bench. Grasp the barbell with your hands shoulder-width apart. Straighten your arms to bring the barbell to a supported position directly above your shoulders.

Movement: Lower the barbell smoothly in 5 seconds to your chest. Without bouncing the bar off your chest, press the weight slowly in 10 seconds until your arms are almost straight. Keep a slight bend in your elbows in the top position. Repeat the 5-second lowering and 10-second pressing for maximum repetitions.

Training tips: Many bodybuilders experiment on the bench press by using wider grips. This is usually a mistake. Since the function of your chest muscles is to move your upper arms across your torso, spacing your hands wider than your shoulders actually shortens your range of movement. Rather than working more of your chest muscles, you're working less of them. For best results on the bench press, keep your hands shoulder-width apart.

Decline Press to Neck with Barbell

Emphasis: The decline press is actually a more productive exercise for the chest than the bench press. When you bring the bar down to your neck you provide a greater range of movement for the involved muscles. And the decline press—because it places your chest muscles, in relationship to your upper arms, in a more favorable line of pull—involves more pectoralis major muscle fibers.

Starting position: You'll need a decline bench with racks for this exercise. Anchor your feet at the high end of the bench. Grasp the barbell with a shoulder-width grip and bring it over your chest.

Movement: Lower the barbell smoothly in 5 seconds, keeping your elbows wide, and lightly touch the bar to your neck. Press the weight slowly in 10 seconds back until your arms are almost straight. Repeat the 5-second lowering and 10-second pressing for maximum repetitions.

Training tips: Use a light weight in this exercise until you develop the required skills. You should get the feel after two or three practice sessions. Then increase the weight appropriately.

BICEPS
Biceps Curl with Barbell

Emphasis: The biceps of your upper arms is the major muscle used in this exercise. The super-slow style makes this an especially productive biceps builder.

Starting position: Take a shoulder-width underhanded grip on a barbell and

stand. Anchor your elbows firmly against the sides of your waist and keep them there throughout the exercise. Lean forward slightly with your shoulders.

Movement: Look down at your hands and curl the weight slowly in 10 seconds. Pause in the top position, but do not move your elbows forward. Keep your hands in front of your elbows. Lower the bar smoothly in 5 seconds. Again, keep your elbows stable against your sides. Repeat the 10-second curling and 5-second lowering for maximum repetitions.

Training tips: Maximize your biceps stimulation by minimizing your body sway. Do not lean forward excessively. Do not lean backward. Do not move your head. Concentrate on your breathing and keep the repetitions slow, smooth, and strict.

Biceps Curl with Dumbbells

Emphasis: The biceps curl with dumbbells works your elbow flexors but also adds the ability to supinate your hands during the movement. Supination (turning your hand from a palm-down to a palm-up position) is a neglected function of the biceps.

Starting position: With a dumbbell in each hand, stand with your arms hanging at your sides. Your palms should be parallel to one another with your thumbs forward. Anchor your elbows firmly against the sides of your waist and keep them there throughout the exercise.

Donkey calf raise: Emphasize the extreme positions for best results.

The bench press can also be performed with a machine.

Lean forward slightly with your shoulders.

Movement: Curl both dumbbells slowly in 10 seconds while simultaneously turning your hands so your palms are facing upward for the last half of the movement. Pause in the top position but do not move your elbows forward. Keep your hands in front of your elbows. Lower the dumbbells smoothly in 5 seconds. Repeat the 10-second curling and 5-second lowering for maximum repetitions.

Training tips: For variety, you can try the alternate dumbbell curl where one dumbbell goes up as the other is lowered. Or you can do the dumbbell curl seated or while leaning against an inclined bench. Regardless of the variation used, make certain that your elbows remain stationary during this movement.

Reverse Curl with Barbell

Emphasis: This exercise involves your biceps, brachialis, and forearm muscles.

Starting position: Take a shoulder-width overhanded grip on a barbell and stand with your arms hanging at your sides. Keep your elbows against your waist throughout the movement.

Movement: Curl the barbell slowly in 10 seconds. Pause in the top position, but do not move your elbows forward. Keep your hands in front of your elbows. Lower the bar smoothly in 5 seconds.

Repeat the 10-second curling and 5-second lowering for maximum repetitions.

Training tips: Perform the reverse curl after you work your biceps, not before. Doing so adds a finishing touch to your arms.

Chin-up

Emphasis: Properly performed, the chin-up is one of the most productive exercises for your biceps and latissimus dorsi.

Starting position: Grasp a high horizontal bar with an underhanded grip and hang. Your hands should be shoulder-width apart.

Movement: Pull your body upward slowly in 10 seconds until your chin is over the bar and your chest is against the bar. Lower your body smoothly in 5 seconds to the hanging position. Repeat the 10-second pulling and 5-second lowering for maximum repetitions.

Training tips: Most bodybuilders employ excessive momentum while doing chin-ups. Slowing the exercise down makes for a drastic reduction in the number of repetitions that you'll be able to do. Five slow repetitions will have more effect than fifteen normal repetitions. For best results, concentrate on your breathing—especially during your final repetitions.

Negative Chin-up

Emphasis: Negative chins also involve your biceps and latissimus dorsi.

This exercise, however, does not utilize the super-slow protocol. Instead, you do the positive work with your legs and the negative work with your upper body.

Starting position: Using a chair or bench for assistance, climb into the top position with your chin over the bar. Use an underhanded grip and space your hands shoulder-width apart.

Movement: Remove your feet from the chair and lower your body slowly in 10 seconds. Make sure you come all the way down to a dead hang. Quickly climb back to the top position with your chin over the bar. Repeat the slow lowering for maximum repetitions.

Training tips: Your strength should increase rapidly on the negative chin-up. Soon you'll be able to strap or hang additional weight around your hips. Here are the guidelines to follow:

During your first several negative repetitions, you should take 10 seconds to lower your body. If you had to, you could stop the downward movement. But don't. Continue to lower in 10 seconds. After five or six repetitions, if the weight is selected correctly, you should be able to control the downward movement, but *not* stop it. When you can no longer control your negative repetition, stop. In other words, the entire lowering portion will be completed in 2 or 3 seconds, in spite of your best efforts to reduce the speed. When you can do ten or more repetitions in good form, add more weight around your hips.

TRICEPS
Triceps Extension with One Dumbbell

Emphasis: This is the best exercise for isolating the triceps of your upper arms.

Starting position: Hold a dumbbell at one end with both hands. Press the dumbbell overhead. Your elbows should be close to your ears.

Movement: Bend your elbows and smoothly lower the dumbbells in 5 seconds behind your neck. Do not move your elbows. Only your forearms and hands should move. Press the dumbbell slowly in 10 seconds back to the starting position. Repeat the 5-second lowering and 10-second raising for maximum repetitions.

Training tips: In the bottom position of this exercise, the triceps is stretched across two joints. Thus, it is vulnerable to strains. Make sure this does not occur by keeping your lower turnarounds smooth and slow.

Dip

Emphasis: The parallel bar dip works your triceps, deltoids, and pectoral muscles.

Starting position: Mount the parallel bars and straighten your arms. Steady your body in the top position.

Movement: Bend your arms and lower your body smoothly in 5 seconds. Stretch comfortably at the bottom. Push

Bent-armed fly with dumbbells: Keep the lowering smooth and the raising slow.

back slowly in 10 seconds to the top position. Repeat the 5-second lowering and 10-second raising for maximum repetitions.

Training tips: The dip, like the chin-up, is an exercise that most body-builders perform using too much momentum. Keep your repetitions slow and you'll concentrate the resistance on your involved muscles.

Negative Dip

Emphasis: Negative dips involve your pushing muscles: triceps, deltoids, and pectoralis majors.

Starting position: Most trainees will require extra resistance added to their body weight for maximum results from negative dips. Place a sturdy chair or bench between the parallel bars. Climb into the top position and straighten your arms. Remove your feet from the chair and stabilize your body.

Movement: Bend your arms and lower your body smoothly in 10 seconds. Stretch comfortably in the bottom position. Climb back to the starting position and straighten your arms. Repeat the slow lowering for maximum repetitions.

Training tips: Keep the time between negative repetitions as brief as possible. Quickly climb back to the top position. Do not take longer than 3 seconds on the climb. In fact, 2 seconds is even better. Taking a longer time between negative repetitions allows your involved muscles a chance to recover partially.

FOREARMS
Wrist Curl with Barbell

Emphasis: This exercise stresses the flexor muscles of your forearms.

Starting position: Grasp a barbell with a palms-up grip. Rest your forearms on your thighs and the back of your hands against your knees, and be seated. Lean forward until the angle between your upper arms and forearms is less than 90 degrees. This position allows you to isolate your forearms more completely.

Movement: Curl your hands slowly in 10 seconds and contract your forearm muscles. Pause briefly. Lower your hands smoothly in 5 seconds. Repeat the 10-second curling and 5-second lowering for maximum repetitions.

Training tips: Since this is such a short range of motion, it's easy to cheat on this exercise. Resist that temptation. Keep your repetitions slow and strict, and your forearms will respond rapidly.

Reverse Wrist Curl with Barbell

Emphasis: Reversing your hands on the barbell emphasizes the extensor muscles of your forearms.

Starting position: Assume the same position as for the wrist curl, except use a palms-down grip.

Movement: Curl the backs of your hands slowly upward in 10 seconds. Pause in the contracted position. Lower smoothly in 5 seconds. Do not move your shoulders or torso forward or backward.

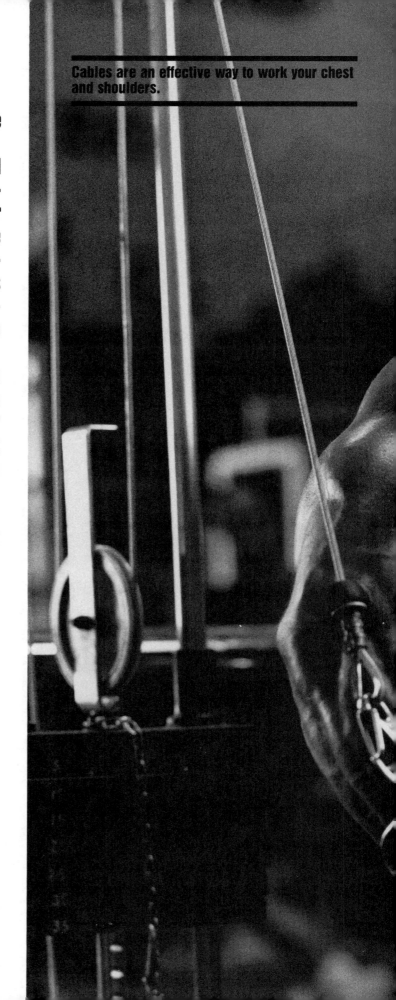

Cables are an effective way to work your chest and shoulders.

Keep them stable. Repeat the 10-second raising and 5-second lowering for maximum repetitions.

Training tips: Most trainees are very weak in their forearm extensors. A light resistance is all that is required to get a super pump from this exercise.

MIDSECTION
Trunk Curl

Emphasis: This is an excellent exercise for your entire abdominal wall.

Starting position: Lie faceup on the floor with your hands behind your head. Keep your chin on your chest. Bring your heels up close to your buttocks and spread your knees. Do not anchor your feet under anything, and don't have a partner hold your knees down. Anchoring your feet brings into action your hip flexors more than your abdominals.

Movement: Curl your shoulders slowly in 10 seconds toward your hips. Only one-third of a standard sit-up can be performed in this manner. When you do this movement correctly, you will feel a powerful contraction in your rectus abdominis muscles. Pause in the contracted position. Lower your trunk smoothly in 5 seconds to the floor. Repeat the 10-second curling and 5-second lowering for maximum repetitions.

Training tips: When eight or more repetitions of the trunk curl can be accomplished in proper form, add a light barbell plate across your chest or behind your head.

Mike Quinn does alternate curls with dumbbells.

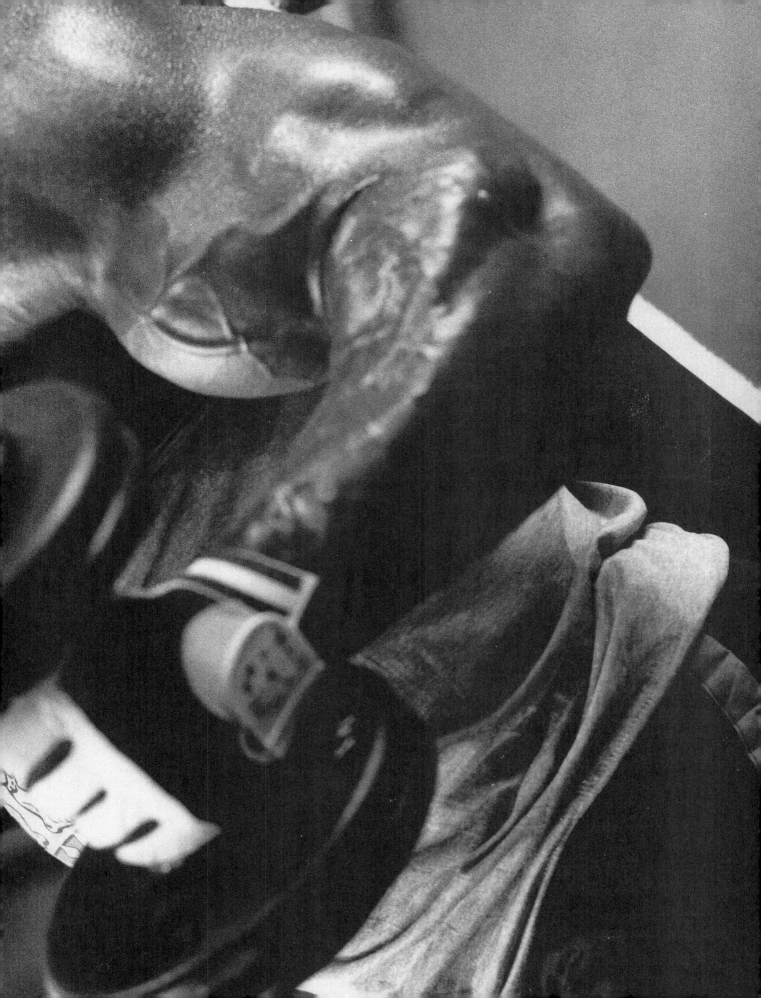

Reverse Trunk Curl

Emphasis: By bringing your hips toward your chest rather than curling your chest and shoulders toward your hips, the reverse trunk curl places extra stress on the lower abdominals.

Starting position: Lie faceup on the floor with your hands on either side of your hips. Bring your thighs on your chest so your knees and hips are in a flexed position.

Movement: Curl your hips toward your chest slowly in 10 seconds by lifting your buttocks and lower back off the floor. At the same time that you lift your buttocks, you must counterbalance your body by pushing down on the floor with your hands and arms. Pause briefly in the top position. Lower your hips smoothly in 5 seconds to the floor. Repeat the 10-second curling and 5-second lowering for maximum repetitions.

Training tips: Concentrate on curling your hips and knees upward by contraction of your abdominals only, rather than allowing momentum to assist you. Remember, you are at the bottom of the movement when your buttocks touch the floor. Do not allow your legs to swing downward past this point. Keep your knees on your chest throughout the movement.

Bent-over extensions with a dumbell activate the contracted position of the triceps.

BIG!

CHAPTER 7
EATING FOR BULK

BIG

There are thousands and thousands of teenage bodybuilders who find it difficult to gain weight. The problem centers around three factors.

One, many teenage boys, because of their widely fluctuating hormones which are related to the maturation process, are overactive. Two, many teenage boys have very inefficient metabolisms. Three, some teenage boys are both overactive and have inefficient metabolisms.

In all three situations, it takes understanding, planning, and applying to gain meaningful body weight. In this chapter, I'll provide you with some basic principles of eating for bulk.

123

Massively thick muscles are the trademark of Nimrod King.

CHECK YOUR FAMILY MEDICAL HISTORY

If you have a family history of heart disease or high blood pressure, you should check with your physician before starting a bulk-building program. Have your blood lipid profiles taken and your blood pressure measured. If any of these values are abnormally high, be sure to involve your physician in any plans for gaining weight.

INCREASE CALORIC CONSUMPTION

Increased caloric consumption is essential for gaining mass. Both muscle and fat contain calories. A pound of muscle registers 600 calories, while a pound of fat carries 3,500 calories. The difference between the calories of muscle and fat reflects the composition of the tissues. Muscle is mostly water and fat is primarily lipids.

The idea behind your bulkbuilding diet is to gain a slight amount of fat as you are building a maximum amount of muscle. Your dietary calories per day must be more than you normally consume, but not excessive to the degree that you significantly increase your percentage of body fat.

A general guideline to follow is to

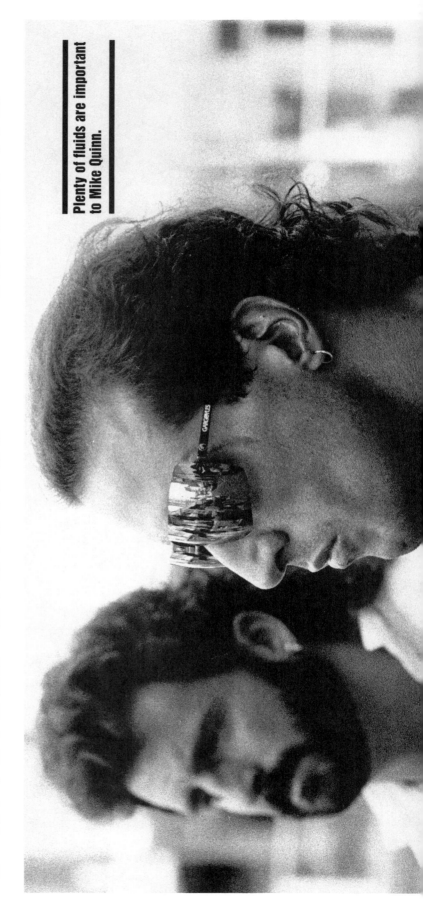

Plenty of fluids are important to Mike Quinn.

124

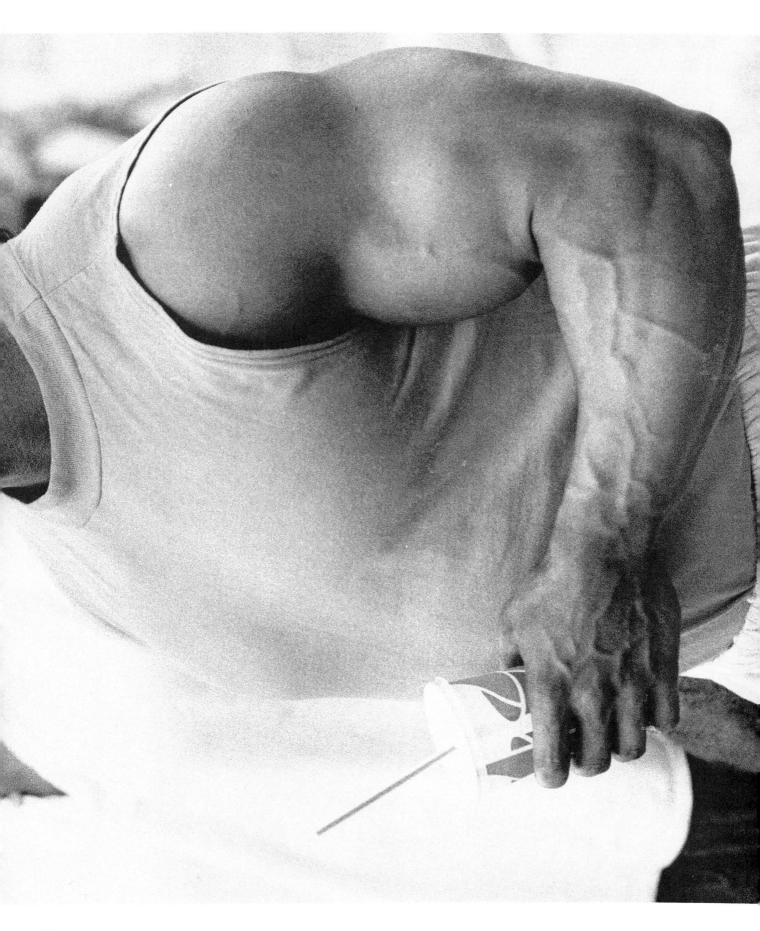

multiply your current body weight in pounds by 20. This provides an estimate for the number of calories per day an average teenage boy would require to keep his body weight stable. The weight-gaining diet should provide energy in excess of body needs by at least 500 calories per day.

Thus, if you weigh 160 pounds, your maintenance energy needs per day are 3,200. To this you'd add 500 more, which would bring the total to 3,700 calories per day.

EAT A BALANCED DIET

Although high-energy consumption is the main objective of this eating plan, care should be taken to keep your foods well balanced. In my opinion, the ideal balanced diet for bodybuilding consists of 59 percent carbohydrates, 28 percent fat, and 13 percent proteins.

The sample menus presented in Part II of this book are ideally balanced according to the Basic Four Food Groups and a 4:4:8:8 ratio. The 4:4:8:8 ratio is a reminder of how much of each food group you should have as a minimum. For example, its basic eating plan for one day translates to:

■ 4 servings from the meat/poultry/fish/legumes (dried beans,

If you're allergic to milk, don't pour it down the drain. A special enzyme can be purchased at the supermarket to add to the milk to make it more digestable.

peas, lentils)/egg group—referred to in abbreviated form as the Meat Group.

- 4 servings from the milk/yogurt/cheese group—referred to as the Milk Group.
- 8 servings from the Fruit/Vegetable Group.
- 8 servings from the Bread/Cereal Group (which includes rice and pasta).

The carbohydrate-rich foods (fruits, vegetables, breads, and cereals) provide lots of vitamins and minerals. Furthermore, the protein-rich foods (meat and milk) supply adequate amino acids for muscular growth. Such a combination, once again, is ideal for getting big.

CONSUME A NUTRITIOUS BREAKFAST

Eating a nutritious breakfast ensures that vitamins, minerals, amino acids, and other nutrients are available in your body early for possible tissue formation. Research has shown that all the constituents for building new tissues must be available simultaneously. Your body is not able to hold what was eaten for breakfast until the rest of the nutrients are eaten for lunch. This a major reason for eating balanced meals.

EAT MORE FREQUENT MEALS

Increased caloric consumption seems to be most easily achieved by adding snacks or mini-meals to the standard three meals a day. Spreading out caloric consumption also helps to ensure optimal energy levels and continuous availability

of amino acids for protein synthesis and recovery from workouts.

CONSUME CALORIE-DENSE FOODS

The following foods are loaded with calories. Consume them liberally.

- Whole milk
- Peanut butter
- Sweetened condensed milk
- Eggs
- Beef steak
- Cheese
- Wheat germ oil
- Ice cream
- Chocolate candy

CONSUME DRIED FRUITS AND NUTS

Dried fruits and nuts are also excellent bulkbuilding foods. Cashews, peanuts, almonds, walnuts, and pecans should be added to your list of recommended foods. And ditto for dried fruits, such as apricots, apples, figs, raisins, prunes, and peaches. These foods are superb snacks.

DRINK MORE MILK

Milk has long been a weight-gaining staple for bodybuilders. A gallon of whole milk contains 2,480 calories. Many a successful bodybuilder in his quest for bulk has drunk a gallon of milk a day for weeks. And that's in addition to consuming three regular meals a day. The best way to drink the milk is to sip it down a cup at a time throughout the day.

Some individuals cannot tolerate milk because their bodies don't produce enough lactase, the stomach enzyme that helps to digest lactose, the sugar in milk. If you feel bloated, or have gas, cramps, or diarrhea after consuming milk, you are probably allergic to it. You can still consume other milk products, such as cheese, yogurt, and enzyme-treated milks.

You'll also find it advantageous to use a blender for milk shakes several times a day. Many of the calorie-dense foods that I've listed lend themselves well to a blender drink.

BE PATIENT

Building bulk for most teenagers will be slow and gradual. This is because the extra calories that are being consumed must be taken into cells and used to synthesize new tissues. These processes take time.

If too many calories are consumed in too short a time, a disproportional amount of the weight gain will be fat. Generally, if you weigh between 125 and 150 pounds, a realistic weight gain goal is from 0.5 to 1.0 pounds per week. If you weigh from 150 to 200 pounds, the goal is from 1.0 to 2.0 pounds per week. Be patient in your eating and exercising, and your results will surprise you.

Lee Haney curbs his appetite with a cup of hot tea.

"Strict dieting can keep you on edge," says Samir Bannout.

The correct combination of diet and exercise has contributed to the bodybuilding success of Marjo Selin.

Mike Ashley is one of the leanest of the professional bodybuilders.

BIG!
PART II
THE HOW

BIG!

CHAPTER 8
SIX-WEEK BULKBUILDING PROGRAM

Shawn Ray's bulk is impressive.

BIG

It had been almost three years since I'd trained twenty-three-year-old Eddie Mueller. Eddie was determined to get his body weight over 190 pounds. We had six weeks of training ahead of us.

The date was June 8, 1989, and I put Eddie through the standard measurements. Before beginning Week 1 of this bulkbuilding program, you should enter your stats on the record sheet on p. 136.

GET A
HELPING HAND

It is difficult to measure yourself accurately. Try to get your training partner to take your measurements in inches, and then you take his.

The skinfold values, which allow

DR. ELLINGTON DARDEN'S SIX-WEEK BULKBUILDING PROGRAM

NAME		AGE	
	BEFORE	AFTER	DIFFERENCE
Date	3 FEB		
Height	6'		
Weight			
CIRCUMFERENCE MEASUREMENTS			
Neck			
Right upper arm			
Left upper arm			
Right forearm			
Left forearm			
Chest			
Waist			
Hips			
Right thigh			
Left thigh			
Right calf			
Left calf			
SKINFOLD MEASUREMENTS			
Right chest			
Right abdomen			
Right thigh			
TOTAL			
PERCENTAGE			

Photographs: front, side, back

The forward raise works the frontal deltoids.

you to determine your percentage of body fat, are best taken with metal calipers. Many gyms utilize the calipers, so you might ask around to locate a pair. Knowledgeable gym personnel will probably assist you in making skinfold evaluations.

I also recommend that you have a set of full-body photographs made of yourself from the front, side, and back—in both normal and posed states. Such photographs can be meaningful in judging your strengths, weaknesses, and overall improvements.

For a complete discussion of how to take before-and-after measurements and photos, please see my book *Massive Muscles in 10 Weeks*, pages 20–24.

THE PLAN

The super-slow, high-intensity exercise program for Eddie was divided into three, two-week segments. Each two-week segment was composed of six workouts: Monday, Wednesday, Friday, and Monday, Wednesday, Friday. Each workout consisted of a total of ten exercises. Some exercises were performed for two sets, but each set was counted as one of the ten exercises. No workout lasted longer than 30 minutes.

The routines remained the same during each segment, but the segments were all different.

During super slow, the positive phase of each repetition should take twice as long as the negative portion.

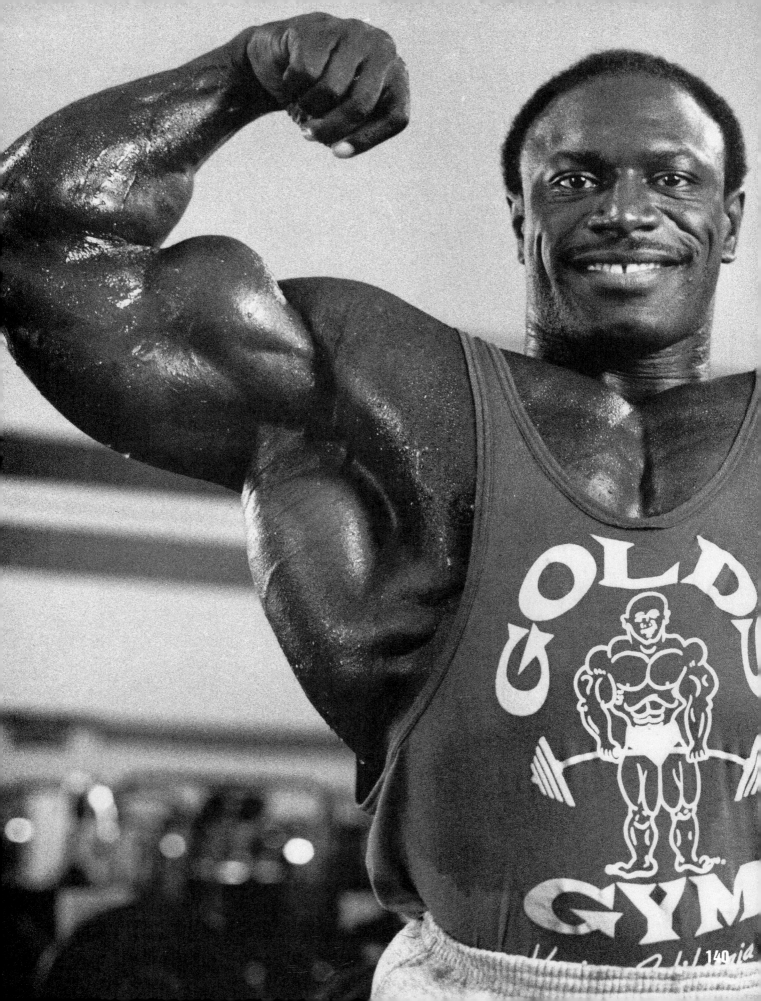

From previously working with Eddie in the *Massive Muscles in 10 Weeks* program, I knew he needed to consume at least 4,000 calories a day to gain weight. Our plan was to start him on 4,400 calories for Weeks 1 and 2, and 4,600 calories for Weeks 3 and 4. If steady progress was being made at the end of Week 4, then we'd up his calories during Weeks 5 and 6 to 4,800 per day.

Eddie's exact exercise routines and food recommendations are listed and described in the next three chapters.

The wide, wide lats of Lee Haney.

The super-slow squat produces astonishing gains.

BIG!

CHAPTER 9

WEEKS 1 AND 2

BIG

"Those super-slow barbell squats are the hardest exercise I've ever done in my entire life," Eddie said approximately 30 minutes after his initial workout and after a pint of chocolate milk had settled his stomach. "And those super-slow chin-ups are almost as bad."

Eddie had just finished his first workout of Week 1 and I knew I'd gotten his attention. A key factor in the success of the program, however, was to *keep* his attention.

"You need to think about breathing," I said as Eddie relaxed on the gym floor. "The lower turnarounds on the squats and chins are especially important. Don't hold your breath. Don't move your head from side to side. Keep your head stable, relax your face, open your mouth, and breathe."

Aaron Baker's chest makes Batman run for cover.

Fruits and vegetables are great sources of carbohydrates.

"I can't seem to get enough air into my lungs," Eddie replied. "The second set of squats was burning my lungs as bad as my legs."

"You've seen that Tom Hanks movie *Turner and Hootch*, haven't you, Eddie?" I asked.

"Sure, that was a great movie."

"Do you remember how Hootch breathed?" I prodded, not waiting for an answer. "He'd let his tongue hang out and he'd breathe rapidly. It's called panting. That's what I want you to get used to doing, Eddie, on all the super-slow exercises."

Eddie reacted with a weird grin that indicated he'd gotten my point. "You want me to pant like Hootch!" he ascertained.

"Practice taking a series of short, rapid breaths with the emphasis on blowing out rather than taking in large gulps of air. Try to ventilate just enough so your breathing never stops."

Eddie was up to the challenge. I could tell I struck a chord that he could easily relate to.

"Sorta like this?" he replied, going through a series of short, forced exhalations that would make a Lamaze class envious, and Hootch feel that he'd found a friend.

"Yeah, that's much better," I said. "That seems to come very naturally to you. But two hints, Eddie: Keep your tongue in your mouth and quit slobbering on the floor."

Each super-slow repetition should be performed as slowly as possible without stopping the movement.

At his next workout Eddie demonstrated his mastery of the superslow breathing technique. As a result, he added almost 10 pounds to his physique during Weeks 1 and 2.

Let's examine the exact eating plan and exercise routine that he followed.

EATING PLAN

If your height and body weight are similar to Eddie's, I recommend that you use the chart on page 152 for 4,400 calories per day as a guideline. Notice that the Basic Four Food Groups, plus other foods, are listed on the left. The recommended daily servings for each food group are listed on the right. In the middle are boxes that correspond to the serving numbers. (For a full description of what constitutes a serving in each group, refer back to the food group table in chapter 7.)

Make fourteen photocopies of the chart. That way you'll have a separate chart for each day that composes Weeks 1 and 2. Get in the habit of checking off the appropriate boxes each time you consume food throughout the day. If you are able to fill up all the boxes in all the food groups, then you can be sure that you've accomplished two important objectives: First, you'll have eaten approximately 4,400 calories. Second, your daily calories will be well balanced among carbohy-

Try to keep your facial contortions to a minimum and you'll better isolate the targeted muscles.

drates (50 to 60 percent), fats (25 to 30 percent), and proteins (12 to 15 percent).

Chapter 10 and chapter 11 have extended charts for 4,600 and 4,800 calories per day. You should apply them in the same manner.

EXERCISE ROUTINE FOR WEEKS 1 AND 2

The correct order of the exercises is on the workout chart. Complete descriptions of specific movements are in chapter 6. Here's a brief comment, however, about each exercise to move you to action.

1. SQUAT WITH BARBELL: There's no doubt that super-slow squats will get your blood moving. Practice your breathing and grind out every possible repetition. Move immediately from the squat to the pullover.

2. PULLOVER WITH ONE DUMBBELL: Try to get a maximum stretch throughout your rib cage and latissimus dorsi during each repetition of this exercise. Take at least a 1-minute break between the finish of the pullover and your second set of squats.

3. SQUAT WITH BARBELL: Use the same weight on the second set of squats that you used on the first set. Also, try to do the same number of repetitions on both sets. Again, after the final repetition, get the squat bar back into the racks, lie across the

DR. ELLINGTON DARDEN'S BULKBUILDING DIET

WEEKS 1 AND 2   (TOTAL CALORIES: 4,400 PER DAY)
FOOD GROUPS

DATE:

RECOMMENDED DAILY SERVINGS

MEAT

7

MILK

7

**FRUIT/
VEGETABLE**

15

**BREAD/
CEREAL**

15

**OTHER
FOODS**

9.75

DR. ELLINGTON DARDEN'S BULKBUILDING ROUTINE

NAME

WEEKS 1 AND 2 SUPER-SLOW PROTOCOL

EXERCISE	DATE	3 FEB					
	BODYWEIGHT						
1. Squat with barbell							
2. Pullover with one dumbbell							
3. Squat with barbell							
4. Pullover with one dumbbell							
5. Leg extension — or — 5. Leg curl							
6. Lateral raise with dumbbells							
7. Dip							
8. Chin-up							
9. Negative dip							
10. Negative chin-up							

NOTE: Perform the exercises inside the brackets with no rest in between.

bench, and start doing pullovers.

4. PULLOVER WITH ONE DUMBBELL: You'll be breathing like a freight train on your pullovers, and that's good. That's no excuse to slack off on the intensity or the repetitions. Afterward, get a big drink of water and walk around for approximately 2 minutes.

5. LEG EXTENSION OR LEG CURL: The leg extension is alternated with the leg curl. Do not do them both during the same workout. On Monday, do the leg extension. On Wednesday, perform the leg curl, and so on.

6. LATERAL RAISE WITH DUMB-BELLS: Be sure to keep your elbows and wrists locked as you perform this great deltoid-building exercise.

7. DIP: Super-slow dips are a real bear. Try to eliminate all momentum from each repetition.

8. CHIN-UP: If dips are a bear, then super-slow chin-ups are a dinosaur. Remember, it's 10 seconds up and 5 seconds down.

9. NEGATIVE DIP: Climb up fast and lower your body slowly. Try to get a good eight repetitions in this exercise.

10. NEGATIVE CHIN-UP: Another eight repetitions in the negative chin-up and you should feel a terrific pump throughout your entire upper body.

Pullovers across a bench intensely work your lats and rib cage.

TRAIN WITH A PARTNER

Ten super-slow exercises may not seem like a demanding workout. But if you've practiced the form according to the guidelines in this book, then you'll know otherwise. The second set of squats, in fact, can make you feel as though you just pushed your car for a mile—uphill!

You should realize by now that a good training partner (or coach) is a must during the initial stages of super slow. You simply cannot concentrate on proper form and push yourself intensely at the same time. Thus, a partner is a valuable asset to the success of super slow. Team up with a friend and practice working with each other. Your results will be much more significant.

Hold the last repetition in the midrange for ten seconds and you'll stimulate more muscle fiber involvement.

157

BIG!

CHAPTER 10

WEEKS 3 AND 4

Maximum success from super-slow training involves a great deal of mental preparation.

![BIG]

Eddie's lower body, primarily because of the super-slow squats, was growing faster than his upper body. Thus, we decided to do the squat and the pullover last, rather than first, in the routine for Weeks 3 and 4. And the double sets were reduced to one. Plus, we added several new movements—bent-over row, bent-armed fly, calf raise, biceps curl, and triceps extension—while still keeping the total exercises to ten.

During Weeks 3 and 4 Eddie's dietary calories were increased by 200 to 4,600 per day. Here's the specific breakdown on the eating and exercising.

EXERCISE ROUTINE FOR WEEKS 3 AND 4

1. NEGATIVE CHIN-UP: You'll be

Robby Robinson's biceps are unsurpassed.

DR. ELLINGTON DARDEN'S BULKBUILDING DIET

WEEKS 3 AND 4   (TOTAL CALORIES: 4,600 PER DAY)   DATE:

FOOD GROUPS	RECOMMENDED DAILY SERVINGS

MEAT

☐ ☐ ☐ ☐ ☐ ☐

☐ ☐

7.25

MILK

☐ ☐ ☐ ☐ ☐ ☐

☐ ☐

7.25

FRUIT/ VEGETABLE

☐ ☐ ☐ ☐ ☐ ☐

☐ ☐ ☐ ☐ ☐ ☐

☐ ☐ ☐

16

BREAD/ CEREAL

☐ ☐ ☐ ☐ ☐ ☐

☐ ☐ ☐ ☐ ☐ ☐

☐ ☐ ☐

16

OTHER FOODS

☐ ☐ ☐ ☐ ☐ ☐

☐ ☐ ☐

10

DR. ELLINGTON DARDEN'S BULKBUILDING ROUTINE

NAME

WEEKS 3 AND 4 SUPER-SLOW PROTOCOL

EXERCISE	DATE					
	BODYWEIGHT					
1. Negative chin-up						
2. Negative dip						
3. Lateral raise with dumbbells — or — 3. Bent-over row with barbell						
4. Bent-armed fly with dumbbells						
5. Calf raise						
6. Leg extension — or — 6. Leg curl						
7. Biceps curl with barbell						
8. Triceps extension with one dumbbell						
9. { Squat with barbell						
10. { Pullover with one dumbbell						

NOTE: Perform the exercises inside the brackets with no rest in between.

stronger at doing negative chins at the beginning of your workout rather than at the end. You'll probably want to hang additional weight around your hips.

2. <u>NEGATIVE DIP:</u> Most trainees are 10 percent stronger in the negative dip than in the negative chin-up. Try adding more resistance for the dip.

3. <u>LATERAL RAISE WITH DUMB-BELLS OR BENT-OVER ROW WITH BARBELL:</u> Use the bent-over row for one workout and the lateral raise for the next.

4. <u>BENT-ARMED FLY WITH DUMB-BELLS:</u> Concentrate on raising and lowering both dumbbells together.

5. <u>CALF RAISE:</u> Practice full-range repetitions and keep your knees locked throughout the movement.

6. <u>LEG EXTENSION OR LEG CURL:</u> Again, apply the leg curl to one workout and the leg extension to the next.

7. <u>BICEPS CURL WITH BARBELL:</u> Keep your elbows stable and you'll feel this exercise intensely in your biceps.

8. <u>TRICEPS EXTENSION WITH ONE DUMBBELL:</u> Your elbow position is also important in working your triceps. With your upper arms in a vertical position, keep your elbows close to your head.

9. <u>SQUAT WITH BARBELL:</u> Even though you'll be doing squats near the end, as opposed to the begin-ning, try to handle the same weight

The last repetitions are the most productive. Do not neglect them.

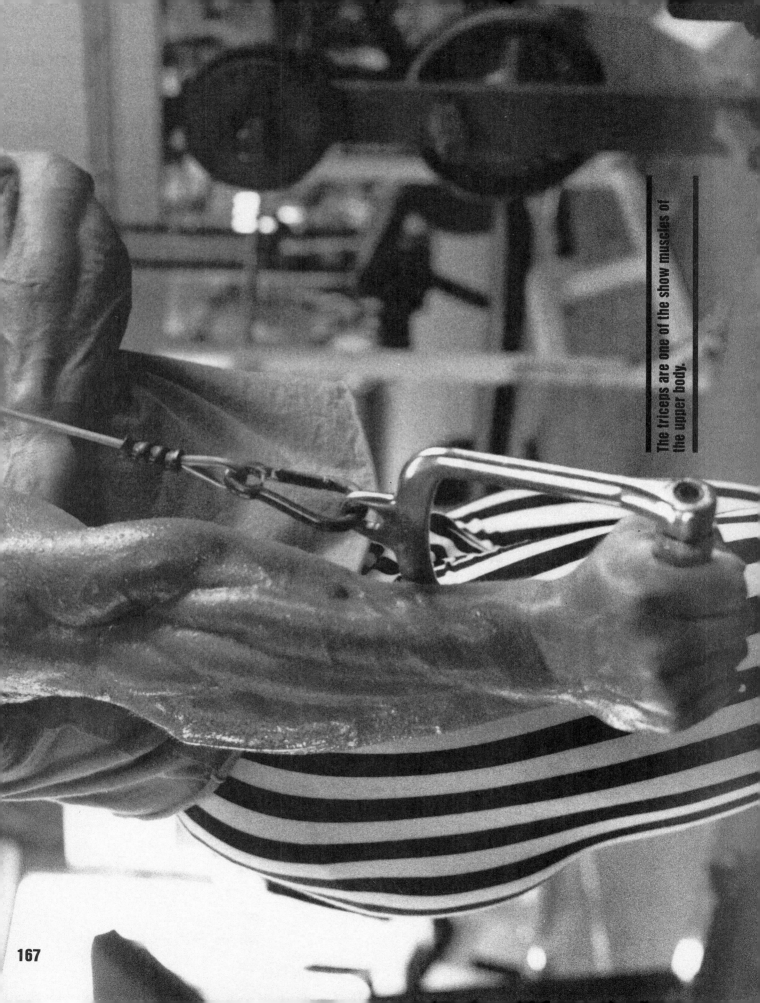

The triceps are one of the show muscles of the upper body.

that you used last week.

10. PULLOVER WITH ONE DUMB-BELL: After the squats, immediately do the pullovers. Remember to emphasize your breathing.

EMPHASIZE CARBOHYDRATES AFTER YOUR WORKOUT

One tip that helped Eddie make better bulkbuilding progress was to get some carbohydrates into his system immediately after his workout. What he found worked best was to eat two bananas and wash them down with a pint of chocolate milk.

Your fatigued muscles seem most responsive to energy storage within the first 30 minutes following your workout. There is a lesser response for the next 10 hours. Thus, your meal after an intense workout should be rich with carbohydrates.

Avoid locking out your elbows on any pressing movement. Stopping just short of straightening your elbows will make the exercise more productive.

Mike Christian spots Phil Hill on the incline fly with dumbbells.

Seated behind neck presses are a great bulkbuilding movement for the deltoids.

BIG!

CHAPTER 11

WEEKS 5 AND 6

The stiff-legged deadlift is one of the best exercises for overall body growth.

BIG

Eddie walked into the gym on Monday afternoon looking bigger than ever. "It's a good thing that it's the middle of July," I thought to myself, because shorts and T-shirts are acceptable summer wear almost anywhere in Dallas. If Eddie were being trained in January or February, keeping him outfitted in warmer clothes would have been a costly nuisance.

"Okay, Eddie, take off your shoes and hop on the scales," I said. "It looks like you've gained a couple of pounds over the weekend."

"I think I did," Eddie replied as he untied his tennis shoes. "I really packed away the food at Caliente's. They had an all-you-can-eat special last night on fajitas."

For those of you who have never had Mexican fajitas, you're missing something. Fajitas are strips of charbroiled beef steak that are served sizzling hot with chopped onions, peppers, tomatoes, and sour cream. These ingredients are as-

A terrific exercise for the upper arms is the one-armed triceps extension.

sembled in a tortilla and quickly consumed.

In the meantime, Eddie had stepped on the scale and was getting a reading. "One eighty-seven and a half. This is the most I've ever weighed, and it's all muscle."

"That may be debatable, Eddie my boy," I said as I reached into my desk drawer and grasped the skin-fold caliper. "Let me take a caliper reading on your waist."

Eddie lumbered over with a smug look on his face. "Okay, caliper this," he said as he lifted his shirt, revealing his midsection.

I could tell by grasping a fold of skin to the right of his navel that Eddie had put on some fat as well as muscle. With the caliper in place the reading was 21 millimeters.

"Well, let's see, Eddie," I said, thumbing through his file. "When you began the program four weeks ago, I calipered your waist at 14 millimeters. Now it's 21. Your body weight has gone from 172.5 to 187.5 for a gain of 15 pounds. Checking the caliper tables shows that roughly 5 of your 15 pounds is fat."

"So you're saying that my 15 pounds of solid muscle," Eddie noted, "is really 5 pounds of fat and 10 pounds of muscle?"

"That's correct, Eddie. I expected you to add a few pounds of fat. In fact, I wanted you to. I certainly didn't want you to get leaner. But I

Laura Crevalle demonstrates a sideway situp that emphasizes the external and internal obliques.

just as certainly didn't want you to put on 5 pounds of fat in four weeks. By the way, how many fajitas did you eat last night?"

"About a dozen, I think," Eddie answered quickly, then paused before adding, "and another dozen the night before, and another dozen the night before that."

"Wait a minute," I said with a raised voice. "I thought you said the special on fajitas was last night?"

"It was, but it was also good for Friday and Saturday."

"So you chowed down on fajitas all three nights?"

"Yep, it was Santa Ana's birthday or something. I couldn't help myself," said Eddie as he fumbled around the gym. "What can I do to get rid of this fat on my waist?"

"You can begin by treating Santa Ana's birthday the same way General Sam Houston did during Texas' revolution," I answered. "Eat the fajitas moderately, fight like hell, and remember the Alamo!"

What I was trying to get across to Eddie was to avoid excessively large meals. Excessively large meals call into action your fat-storing mechanism. Your body recognizes a massive amount of calories as a possible "feast-then-famine" situation. "Something may be wrong soon," says your body, and it becomes an efficient fat maker and preserver.

Since an average-sized fajita

You never outgrow your need for leg extensions.

with trimmings has about 250 calories, Eddie consumed at least 3,000 calories for three consecutive nights. When we calculated his daily caloric consumption for Week 4, it came to 5,700 calories per day. That was 1,100 more calories per day than the recommended 4,600. No wonder he gained several pounds of fat over the last week.

Eddie was still adding muscle to his body at a rate of over 2 pounds per week, so I did not want to reduce his calories drastically. I figured the recommended 4,800 calories per day would be about right (see p. 184).

During Weeks 5 and 6, I also modified his exercise routine. I added the leg press in place of the squat and the upright row instead of the lateral raise. Included in the new routine were two midsection exercises.

EXERCISE ROUTINE FOR WEEKS 5 AND 6

1. <u>LEG PRESS:</u> The primary difference between the leg press and the squat is that the leg press involves a shorter range of movement around the hip joints. Like the squat, however, it is important to emphasize slow, smooth turnarounds at both ends. After the last repetition, quickly lie across a bench and do the pullover.

FLEX

45LBS

WORLD CLASS

DR. ELLINGTON DARDEN'S BULKBUILDING DIET

WEEKS 5 AND 6   (TOTAL CALORIES: 4,800 PER DAY)   **DATE:**

FOOD GROUPS   **RECOMMENDED DAILY SERVINGS**

MEAT

☐ ☐ ☐ ☐ ☐ ☐
☐ ☐

7.5

MILK

☐ ☐ ☐ ☐ ☐ ☐
☐ ☐

7.5

FRUIT/ VEGETABLE

☐ ☐ ☐ ☐ ☐ ☐
☐ ☐ ☐ ☐ ☐ ☐
☐ ☐ ☐ ☐ ☐

17

BREAD/ CEREAL

☐ ☐ ☐ ☐ ☐ ☐
☐ ☐ ☐ ☐ ☐ ☐
☐ ☐ ☐ ☐ ☐

17

OTHER FOODS

☐ ☐ ☐ ☐ ☐ ☐
☐ ☐ ☐ ☐

10.5

DR. ELLINGTON DARDEN'S BULKBUILDING ROUTINE

NAME

WEEKS 5 AND 6 SUPER-SLOW PROTOCOL

EXERCISE	DATE / BODYWEIGHT					
1. Leg press						
2. Pullover with one dumbbell						
3. Calf raise						
4. Leg curl						
or						
4. Leg extension						
5. Bent-armed fly with dumbbells						
6. Negative dip						
7. Upright row with barbell						
8. Biceps curl with barbell						
9. Negative chin-up						
10. Trunk curl						
or						
10. Stiff-legged deadlift with barbell						

NOTE: Perform the exercises inside the brackets with no rest in between.

2. PULLOVER WITH ONE DUMBBELL: Do as many super-slow pullovers as possible and try one more. Walk around for a minute as you recover and ready yourself for the calf raise.

3. CALF RAISE: Because of the short range of movement employed in this exercise, you can use a heavy weight. The idea is to use as much resistance as possible without compromising your strict form.

4. LEG CURL OR LEG EXTENSION: When the leg curl is performed after the calf raise, more emphasis than normal is placed on your calves. During your next workout, do the leg extension instead of the leg curl.

5. BENT-ARMED FLY WITH DUMB-BELLS: This exercise effectively pre-exhausts your pectorals for the negative dip. When you cannot do the fly, sit up, place the dumbbells on the floor, and run to the dip bars.

6. NEGATIVE DIP: The negative dip will carry your pre-exhausted pectoral muscles to a deeper level of growth stimulation. Lower your body very slowly during each movement and always try to do one more repetition.

7. UPRIGHT ROW WITH BARBELL: The upright row is sandwiched between two pre-exhaustion cycles. Your deltoids will feel the effect of this slow, multiple-joint exercise.

8. BICEPS CURL WITH BARBELL: Squeeze out as many super-slow repetitions as possible. Then move quickly to the chinning bar.

9. NEGATIVE CHIN-UP: Your biceps, since they are in a pre-exhausted state, will feel intensely each of these negative repetitions. Continue the lowering until you can no longer control the descend.

10. TRUNK CURL OR STIFF-LEGGED DEADLIFT: The trunk curl works your waist and the deadlift involves your lower back. Alternate them during your workouts for Weeks 5 and 6.

RESULT PRODUCING

None of the routines in Weeks 1 through 6 should take longer than 30 minutes to complete. Remember, it's not the *amount* of exercise that builds massive muscles. It's the *intensity* of the exercise that's most important. Thus, you should always look for ways to make your exercise harder and briefer rather than easier and longer.

All of the routines that you've been following for the last six weeks are king-sized steps in the harder and briefer direction. Such training stimulates muscular growth. How much depends not only on your training, but on your genetics, nutritional status, recovery ability, and overall health. In the next chapter, you can compare your results to Eddie's.

Dips stress all the pushing muscles of the upper body.

BIG!

CHAPTER 12
OVERALL RESULTS

Mike Quinn psychs up for a set of behind neck chins.

After you've completed this six-week bulkbuilding program, you'll want to retake your initial measurements and evaluate your results. Turn back to chapter 8 and get your training partner to measure you in the same spots according to the listings. Record your after-measurements next to the before, and determine the difference between each pair. Now compare your results with Eddie's.

Summing the twelve before-and-after differences revealed that Eddie gained 18⅞ total inches. Most prominent among these measurements was the 5 inches he put on his chest and the 4⅞ inches he added to his thighs. He also increased each upper arm by ¾ of an inch.

EDDIE'S RESULTS

Below is a listing of Eddie Mueller's before-and-after measurements:

EDDIE'S MEASUREMENTS

BODY SITE	BEFORE	AFTER	DIFFERENCE
Neck	15⅝	16⅜	¾
Right upper arm	15	15¾	¾
Left upper arm	15⅛	15⅞	¾
Right forearm	12⅝	13⅛	½
Left forearm	12⅝	13⅜	¾
Chest	40½	45½	5
Waist	32¼	34	1¾
Hips	38⅛	40¼	2⅛
Right thigh	23⅛	25⅝	2½
Left thigh	23¼	25⅝	2⅜
Right calf	15⅛	15¾	⅝
Left calf	15¼	16	¾
TOTAL INCHES GAINED			18⅞

Nimrod King is known for his big arms and big chest.

MUSCLE AND FAT CALCULATIONS

Eddie's body weight and percentage of body fat were also interesting. At twenty-three years of age and a height of 5 feet 8¾ inches, Eddie weighed 172½ pounds at the start of the program. At the conclusion of the six-week course, he weighed 192 pounds. In six weeks he gained 19½ pounds, or an average of 3¼ pounds per week. But as I mentioned at the start of chapter 11, all 19½ pounds of his body weight was not muscle. The amount of fat he put on was determined by comparing his skinfold values below.

Eddie's Skinfold Values

	BEFORE (in millimeters)	AFTER (in millimeters)
Chest	4.5	6.0
Waist	14.0	18.0
Thigh	6.0	6.5
Total	24.5	30.5
PERCENTAGE OF BODY FAT	6.9	8.8

Eddie increased the sum of his three skinfold readings from 24.5 to 30.5 millimeters. Using a special nomogram, these figures convert to 6.9 percent and 8.8 percent body fat. He put on 1.9 percent body fat over the six-week program. This converts to a 5-pound fat gain.

In other words, of the 19½ pounds of body weight that Eddie gained, 5 pounds of it was fat and 14½ pounds was muscle. Most of his fat accumulated around his waistline, as these measurements increased by 1¾ inches. Eddie could have probably avoided some of this stored fat if he had been more careful about his calorie counting during the fourth week.

Calculate your muscle and fat gains and compare them to Eddie's.

PHOTOGRAPHS

Relaxed and posed photographs are one of the best ways to evaluate the improvements in your physique over the last six weeks. Be sure to standardize as much as possible your poses, background, lighting, and size of prints.

In comparing your pictures, it may be helpful to make photocopies of the photographs. With photocopies you can measure, mark, and encircle certain muscle groups with appropriate notations. Doing so will be helpful in making meaningful evaluations.

FOR WOMEN, TOO

It is true that women do not have as much muscle-building potential as men. But they can make steady progress, and this progress can be measured and photographed.

As an example, I supervised Karen McClung—a twenty-five-year-

WORLD CLASS BARBELL

45 LBS

Bent-over row: Pull the bar slowly to your waist.

In six weeks, Eddie Mueller added 19½ pounds to his body.

195

The Six-Week Bulkbuilding program increased Eddie's chest by 5 inches and his thighs by 4⅞ inches.

Phil Williams displays a well-conditioned physique for the camera of Chris Lund

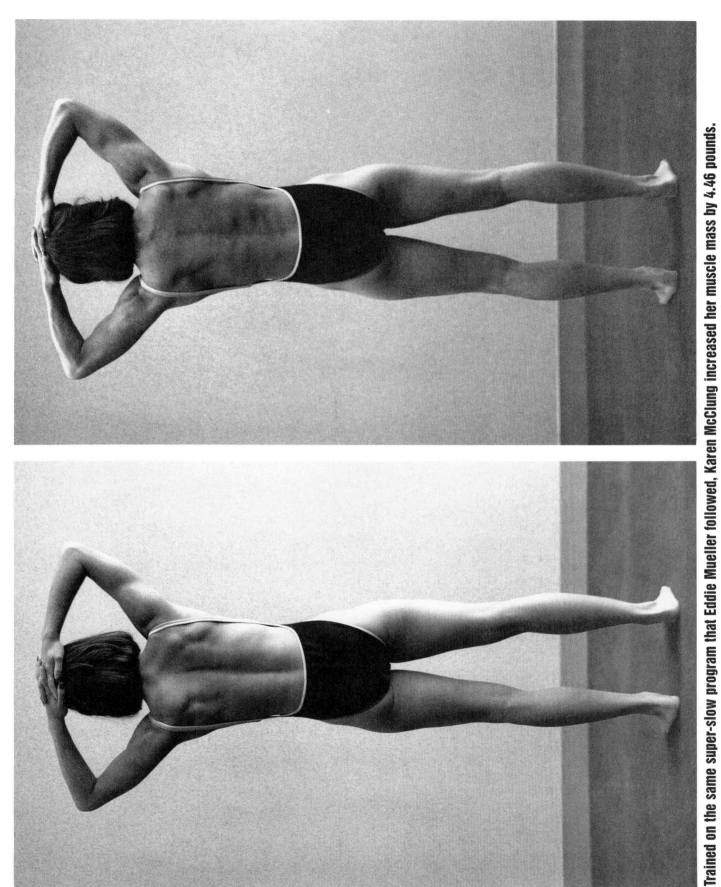

Trained on the same super-slow program that Eddie Mueller followed, Karen McClung increased her muscle mass by 4.46 pounds.

old MBA student at Southern Methodist University—through the same super-slow course that Eddie completed. Karen started the program weighing 127.2 pounds at a height of 5 feet 5¼ inches. Her body fat level was 8.6 percent, which was very lean for a woman.

Karen's bodybuilding potential was similar to Eddie's. On a one to ten scale, with one being very low, five being average, and ten being very high, both Karen and Eddie had a genetic potential of 7.5. While 7.5 is not in the Mr. or Ms. Olympia category, it is significantly above average. Thus, I expected Karen to respond to the training with significant progress and noticeable changes to her body.

Karen was trained in a similar fashion as Eddie, and none of her workouts lasted longer than 30 minutes. Naturally, her food intake was less than Eddie's. During Weeks 1 and 2, Karen consumed 2,800 calories per day. This was increased to 3,000 calories per day for the middle two weeks and 3,200 calories for Weeks 5 and 6.

Karen made steady progress. During the six-week program, her body weight increased from 127.2 to 130.5, a gain of 3.3 pounds. Re-

markably, her percentage of body fat decreased from 8.6 to 7.5 percent. She actually got leaner on an average of 3,000 calories per day. Thus, even though Karen gained 3.3 pounds of body weight, her muscle mass increase was 4.46 pounds, since she lost 1.16 pounds of fat.

You'll be able to see Karen's muscular gains by looking at her before-and-after photographs. You'll notice significant improvements in her arms and torso. In six weeks, she added ¾ of an inch to each upper arm and 1⅝ inches across her chest and back.

If I had started Karen on 3,200 calories per day, instead of 2,800, I believe she would have made even better progress. Evidently, the muscle-building process is facilitated by consuming slightly more calories than you require each day rather than eating slightly below your energy needs.

MAKING MORE PROGRESS

Have you successfully reached some of your bulkbuilding goals? Would you like to get even bigger?

Chapter 13 details how to continue with the program and keep your muscles growing at a steady rate.

Women have the identical number of skeletal muscles as men. The requirements for stimulating muscles to grow is also the same for both men and women.

BIG!

CHAPTER 13
GETTING BIGGER!

The mechanics that made you big should be employed to make you BIGGER.

BIG

High-intensity training makes a severe demand on your recovery ability. After six weeks of super-slow exercising, a brief layoff will prove helpful to you in making further progress.

Starting today, do not train for a week. Get plenty of rest and relaxation. Concentrate on something other than bodybuilding. But continue to eat well. The combination of these factors will replenish your energy reserves and your recovery ability.

After a one-week layoff, you'll be ready to start back training. Before you do, let's return to Eddie's results the six-week bulkbuilding program that you've just completed.

Of the three two-week segments, the routine used during Weeks 1 and 2 was the most productive at increasing Eddie's body weight.

Even if the three different routines were exactly equal in intensity, you'd still expect Eddie's week-by-week weight gain to decrease

Squats are one of the key ingredients in getting bigger.

Lee Haney understands the importance of sticking to a few basic exercises in successful bulkbuilding.

Vince Taylor has the genetics to win the Mr. Olympia.

slightly as he gets closer to his goal. The fact that his weight gain during Weeks 1 and 2 was disproportionately large, compared to the other two-week segments, indicates its effectiveness.

"The first routine was a real killer," remembered Eddie. "I could actually feel myself growing each day."

I concur with Eddie. Two sets of squats, pullovers, chins, and dips cover the entire body in a simple, brief, effective routine. Over the last year, I've supervised several other bodybuilders on the same routine and each of them has made great gains for a period of one to eight weeks.

If you've followed the program exactly as directed, you'll probably agree that this first routine got your attention more than the others. Your greatest rate of growth probably occurred during the initial two weeks. Thus, to get even bigger, I'd recommend that you concentrate almost exclusively on using the first routine—with certain modifications—for the next six weeks.

STICK WITH TEN EXERCISES

It is a little-recognized fact that as you get bigger and stronger, the less overall exercise you require for growth stimulation. While your muscular strength can be increased by 300 percent or more before you

Slow exercise is not fun. But it is enormously productive.

Remember, those last few repetitions are the most important.

reach your genetic potential, your recovery ability does *not* improve in proportion to your strength. Your recovery ability increases only 50 percent. As you get stronger, you must perform less exercise. Less exercise, but with heavier resistance and thus higher intensity, is the secret to making continued progress in your bulkbuilding.

With this in mind, here's how I'd modify the routine during the next six weeks. The basic super-slow workout is as follows:

1. Squat with barbell
2. Pullover with one dumbbell
3. Squat with barbell
4. Pullover with one dumbbell
5. Your choice of exercise
6. Your choice of exercise
7. Dip
8. Chin-up
9. Negative dip
10. Negative chin-up

Perform the listed exercises in the same manner as you did previously. The fifth and sixth exercises are optional according to your specific weaknesses. If your calves are lagging behind, work them here. Or if you want to concentrate on your waist, you could do the trunk curl and reverse trunk curl in these slots. If you decide to emphasize your upper arms and forearms, work them last. Just slide the last four exercises up and move five and six to the nine and ten positions.

Leg extensions and squats are two of the best exercises for your lower body.

It is best to stick to the same optional exercises for at least a week. Then you may substitute two more movements in the slots.

DECREASE YOUR FREQUENCY

Your frequency of training should decrease slightly with each two-week period. Here's the recommended schedule:

Weeks 1 and 2   Six workouts:
Monday, Wednesday, Friday
Monday, Wednesday, Friday

Weeks 3 and 4   Five workouts:
Monday, Thursday, Saturday
Tuesday, Friday

Weeks 5 and 6   Four workouts:
Monday, Thursday
Monday, Thursday

Thus, your workouts per each two-week period descend from six to five to four. As you get stronger—and you should by 5 percent in each exercise each week—you get longer rest cycles, which allow your stimulated muscles more time to recover and grow. Furthermore, such a schedule is the best way to prevent overtraining.

SPECIALIZED SUPER-SLOW ROUTINES

After you've completed another six-week program combined with a week layoff, you should be ready to try various specialized routines. I cover such routines thoroughly in *Super High-Intensity Bodybuilding, Big Arms in Six Weeks,* and *100 High-Intensity Ways to Improve Your Bodybuilding.* You may order them by using page 223 in this book. Some of the best routines are listed on following pages.

Note: Perform the exercises inside the brackets with no rest in between.

SUPER SLOW ROUTINE 1: THIGHS

1. Leg curl
2. Leg press
3. Leg extension
4. Squat
5. Calf raise
6. Bent-over row
7. Bench press
8. Upright row
9. Press behind neck
10. Trunk curl

SUPER SLOW ROUTINE 2: THIGHS

1. Leg press
2. Leg extension
3. Squat
4. Leg curl
5. Stiff-legged deadlift
6. Decline press to neck
7. Lat machine pulldown
8. Lateral raise
9. Biceps curl
10. Triceps extension

SUPER SLOW ROUTINE 3: CALVES

1. Leg curl
2. Calf raise
3. Leg curl
4. Donkey calf raise
5. Leg extension
6. Lateral raise
7. Shoulder shrug
8. Dip
9. Chin-up
10. Reverse trunk curl

SUPER SLOW ROUTINE 4: CALVES

1. Calf raise
2. Leg press
3. Donkey calf raise
4. Bent-armed pullover
5. Press behind neck
6. Lat machine pulldown
7. Bench press
8. Biceps curl
9. Triceps extension
10. Stiff-legged deadlift

SUPER SLOW ROUTINE 5: SHOULDERS

1. Lateral raise
2. Press behind neck
3. Lateral raise
4. Upright row
5. Squat
6. Leg extension
7. Leg curl
8. Bench press
9. Bent-over row
10. Trunk curl

SUPER SLOW ROUTINE 6: SHOULDERS

1. Upright row
2. Lateral raise
3. Press behind neck
4. Upright row
5. Lateral raise
6. Press behind neck
7. Leg extension
8. Leg curl
9. Negative chin-up
10. Negative dip

SUPER SLOW ROUTINE 7: BACK

1. Straight-armed pullover
2. Chin-up
3. Bent-armed pullover
4. Negative chin-up
5. Squat
6. Upright row
7. Dip
8. Biceps curl
9. Triceps extension
10. Stiff-legged deadlift

SUPER SLOW ROUTINE 8: BACK

1. Bent-over row
2. Bent-armed pullover
3. Lat machine pulldown
4. Negative chin-up
5. Leg extension
6. Leg curl
7. Bent-armed fly
8. Shoulder shrug
9. Bench press
10. Reverse trunk curl

SUPER SLOW ROUTINE 9: CHEST

1. Bent-armed fly
2. Bench press
3. Bent-armed fly
4. Negative dip
5. Bent-over row
6. Bent-armed pullover
7. Triceps extension
8. Biceps curl
9. Leg extension
10. Squat

SUPER SLOW ROUTINE 10: CHEST

1. Bench press
2. Bent-armed fly
3. Decline press to neck
4. Negative dip
5. Lat machine pulldown
6. Straight-armed pullover
7. Press behind neck
8. Reverse curl
9. Leg curl
10. Leg press

SUPER SLOW ROUTINE 11: ARMS

1. Biceps curl
2. Negative chin-up
3. Triceps extension
4. Negative dip
5. Leg extension
6. Leg curl
7. Lateral raise
8. Bent-armed fly
9. Wrist curl
10. Reverse wrist curl

SUPER SLOW ROUTINE 12: ARMS

1. Press behind neck
2. Triceps extension
3. Negative dip
4. Lat machine pulldown
5. Biceps curl with dumbells
6. Negative chin-up
7. Leg press
8. Calf raise
9. Upright row
10. Trunk curl

MORE IS NOT BETTER

Try any of these specialized routines for approximately two weeks. Because of the unusual demands placed on a targeted muscle group, as well as your body's recovery ability, more than six consecutive workouts on one routine would probably lead to overtraining. To prevent this from occurring, simply switch to another specialized routine for a different body part. Remember, more is not better when it applies to super-slow, high-intensity exercise.

Strive to make your exercises harder, not easier—briefer, not longer—and your bodybuilding results will be outstanding.

BIG!

CONCLUSION

Think BIG!
Get BIG!
Stay BIG!

Question: What's the fastest, most efficient way to get BIG?

Answer: The super-slow, high-intensity program presented in this book.

By now, you should be a believer.

BE A WINNER. GET *BIG!*

GETTING *BIGGER* MEANS NEVER EVER GIVING UP.